The IEEE 802.11 Handbook

A Designer's Companion

Authored by

Bob O'Hara
Al Petrick

Published by
Standards Information Network
IEEE Press
The Institute of Electrical and Electronics Engineers, Inc.

http://standards.ieee.org

Trademarks and disclaimers

IEEE believes the information in this publication is accurate as of its publication date; such information is subject to change without notice. IEEE is not responsible for any inadvertent errors.

Library of Congress Cataloging-in-Publication Data

O'Hara, Bob, 1956-
  The IEEE 802.11 handbook: a designer's companion / authored by
    Bob O'Hara and Al Petrick.
        p.   cm.
  ISBN 0-7381-1855-9 (paperback : alk. paper) —ISBN 0-7381-1857-5 (pdf)
      1. Local Area Networks (Computer networks)—Standards. 2. Wireless
  communication systems. I. Petrick, Al, 1957- II. Title.

  TK5105.7 O37 1999
  621.382'1—dc21
                                                              99-057887
                                                                    CIP

The Institute of Electrical and Electronics Engineers, Inc.
3 Park Avenue, New York, NY, 10016-5997, USA

Review Policy

The information contained in IEEE Press/Standards Information Network publications is reviewed and evaluated by peer reviewers of relevant IEEE Technical Societies, Standards Committees and/or Working Groups, and/or relevant technical organizations. The authors addressed all of the reviewers' comments to the satisfaction of both the IEEE Standards Information Network and those who served as peer reviewers for this document.

The quality of the presentation of information contained in this publication reflects not only the obvious efforts of the authors, but also the work of these peer reviewers. The IEEE Press acknowledges with appreciation their dedication and contribution of time and effort on behalf of the IEEE.

To order IEEE Press publications, call 1-800-678-IEEE.

Print: ISBN 0-7381-1855-9   SP1118
PDF: ISBN 0-7381-1857-5   SS1118

See other standards and standards-related product listings at:
http://standards.ieee.org/

For teaching me that a little hard work never hurt anyone and for being there every time I have needed them, I dedicate this book to my parents, Bob and Shirley.

- Bob O'Hara

To my parents, Albert and Marge, who have provided me with loving care and taught me the values of life. Also, to my wife and best friend, Patricia, for her loving support, understanding, and patience throughout the writing process, for which I'm forever grateful.

- Al Petrick

Acknowledgment

We wrote this book as a guide for those who will implement interoperable IEEE 802.11 2.4 GHz and 5 GHz wireless LAN (WLAN) products. We were fortunate enough to be part of the IEEE 802.11 Working Group for the past 7 years as chairs and active participants. We would like to thank all of our engineering colleagues who have worked so passionately in the development of the IEEE 802.11 2.4 GHz and 5 GHz WLAN standards and to those who have inspired us to undertake the writing of this book. It gives us great pleasure to have worked with some of the finest, and most creative and innovative engineering professionals in the standards-setting process.

We would like to thank the external reviewers who have commented on the material throughout the process. Their evaluation of the technical content of the handbook has helped us clarify our thinking and make sure we included topics that were core to the physical layer, MAC layer, and for practical system implementations. The reviewers' names and affiliations are listed below.

Naftali Chayat, BreezeCom

Darwin Engwer, Nortel Networks

Ian Gifford, M/A-COM, an AMP Division

Migdat Hodzic, Cadence Design Systems

Gregory Rawlins, Signal Technologies, Inc.

Matt Shoemake, Alantro Communications

Pradeep K. Singh, MIL 3, Inc.

Mark Webster, Intersil Corporation

And finally, we want to thank Yvette Ho Sang and the editorial team at IEEE Press for guiding us throughout the writing process.

Bob O'Hara

Al Petrick

About the Authors

Bob O'Hara is the president and founder of Informed Technology, Inc., a company that specializes in strategic, technology, and network consulting. He is actively involved in the development of networking, telecommunications, and computing standards and products. His areas of expertise are: network and communication protocols and their implementation, operating systems, system specification and integration, standards development, cryptography and its application, strategy development, and product definition. Mr. O'Hara has been involved with the development of the IEEE 802.11 WLAN standard since 1992. He is the technical editor of that standard and chairman of the revisions and regulatory extensions task groups.

Prior to starting Informed Technology, Mr. O'Hara worked for Advanced Micro Devices in both senior engineering and management positions for the I/O and Network Products Division and in the Advanced Development Lab, as well as engineering positions at Fairchild Space and Communications and TRW Defense and Space Systems Group. He Graduated with a BSEE from the University of Maryland in 1978.

Al Petrick is Director of Marketing and Business Development at ParkerVision for the wireless product line. Mr. Petrick's experience includes over 20 years of combined marketing and systems engineering in wireless communications with emphasis on semiconductor technology. Prior to ParkerVision, Mr. Petrick held senior management marketing and business development positions at Intersil Semiconductor. He successfully pioneered semiconductor technology for the WLAN market from inception through announcement. Mr. Petrick serves as Vice-Chair of the IEEE 802.11 WLAN standards committee. Mr. Petrick published various marketing and technical papers on wireless communications and is a distinguished writer with leading wireless trade journals and market and financial analysts. Mr. Petrick holds a BSET from Rochester Institute of Technology, Rochester, New York and an MBA from Rollins College, Winter Park, Florida. He also studied business-strategies at Northwestern University Kellogg Graduate School of Management.

Foreword

Since the publication of the IEEE 802.11 WLAN standard, many equipment manufacturers have entered the market with interoperable WLAN systems. In September 1999, the IEEE-SA Standards Board approved the 2.4 GHz, 11 Mbps 802.11b and 5 GHz, 54 Mbps 802.11a extensions. However, standards are written as specifications for interoperable products and not as handbooks for obtaining a thorough understanding of the protocol. It is impossible to include in the standards all the reasons for decisions taken to get the standard ratified.

The only people who could write a handbook with the qualities I have in mind are those that have followed the standards process from the beginning. I applaud Bob O'Hara and Al Petrick for taking on the task of writing this handbook. Bob and Al have been very instrumental throughout the development of the IEEE 802.11 standard and are recognized for their contributions and technical leadership. This book is a first-of-a-kind and provides a perfect balance of information for embracing the physical and MAC layers of the standard.

I expect *The IEEE 802.11 Handbook: A Designer's Companion* to become a standard reference for every WLAN systems engineer and anticipate the reader will find this text extremely useful.

Vic Hayes
Chairman, IEEE P802.11, Standards WG for Wireless LANs
Lucent Technologies Nederland B. V.
Zadelstede 1-10
The Netherlands

Preface

This book from Bob and Al is very timely. Wireless LANs are exploding in popularity. The WLAN industry is taking off and expanding beyond its vertical niche market roots. One of the key drivers of this new market expansion for WLANs is the IEEE 802.11 standard. Simply having a WLAN standard was not enough to spark the industry. IEEE 802.11 has been around since June of 1997. The IEEE 802.11b High-Rate Physical Layer extension enabled us to deliver 11 Mbps and products conforming to that standard have been shipping for a while. Wireless LANs have finally hit the right price and performance to appeal to a broader market. Breaking the 10 Mbps barrier makes IEEE 802.11 LANs appealing for enterprise applications. Home networking is becoming more popular, and WLANs are an attractive option. By the time you read this, you will be able to purchase an IEEE 802.11-compliant, 11 Mbps consumer WLAN adapter for $99 or less. Wireless LANs are ready for prime time and IEEE 802.11 made it happen.

The IEEE 802.11 standard represents many years of work from a global team of engineers. One of the challenges of developing the IEEE 802.11 standard was bringing together experts from two different disciplines —analog radio design and network protocol design. We had many arguments about whether this is a radio standard or a network standard. Very clearly, IEEE 802.11 is a network standard. That is the whole point. Because IEEE 802.11 fits into the IEEE 802 framework, systems conforming to the standard can be added to existing networks transparently. IEEE 802.11 WLANs will support the network protocols and applications that were developed for the other IEEE 802 LAN standards over the past 25 years. So IEEE 802.11 is a network standard that happens to have a radio physical layer. This book benefits from the fact that Bob and Al are experts in both of these disciplines. They have a deep understanding of the material gained through their many years of contribution to the standard.

The standard was over 400 pages when initially published, and recently two new physical layer extensions were added. Bob and Al help the reader navigate through the complexity of the standard and focus on the core issues. This book is a great guide to the standard for anyone developing IEEE 802.11 products or those simply wanting to gain a better understanding of the standard.

Enjoy!

Phil Belanger
Chairman of the Wireless Ethernet Compatibility Alliance, www.wi-fi.com
Co-Author of the DFWMAC protocol, the proposal that was used as the basis for the IEEE 802.11 MAC

Introduction

A number of books have been written in the last several years on the topic of
WLANs. Why is it necessary to bring another one to your shelves? We believe
that, with the advent of the IEEE 802.11 standard for WLANs, the consolidation
of the WLAN market will commence. Therefore, it is important that WLAN
designers, network planners and administrators, and users understand the operation and application of IEEE 802.11. This handbook will provide the detail
required to attain that understanding.

With the advent of IEEE 802.11 WLANs, an era of multivendor product competition and innovation has begun, similar to that begun by the adoption of the
IEEE 802.3 standard. This era is closing the door on proprietary WLANs that
have seen limited acceptance, mostly in vertical applications such as warehous-
ing, inventory control, and retail. The goal of the IEEE 802.11 Working Group
was to define a complete WLAN system that would allow the use of WLANs in
all application areas, including the typical horizontal application of corporate
LANs, where wired LANs are found today. It is our belief that the working
group has been successful in reaching this goal.

There are two major components of the WLAN described by IEEE 802.11, the
mobile station and the access point (AP). Going well beyond what other IEEE
802 standards have done in the past, IEEE 802.11 defines a complete management protocol between the mobile station and AP. This management protocol
makes it possible for a single IEEE 802.11 WLAN to comprise equipment from
many vendors, marking true multivendor interoperability.

There is a huge amount of information in the IEEE 802.11 standard and its
extensions. Finding the information required in a short time can be challenging.
To help meet the challenge, a mapping between the information in the standards
and that presented in this handbook is given here. IEEE standards are divided
into clauses and annexes. Information in the standard is referred to by the clause
and annex in which it is found. This book is divided into chapters. Information
in this book is referred to by the chapter in which it is found.

Clauses 1 through 4 of the standard contain a brief overview of the standard,
other references that are required to implement the standard, definitions of
terms, and the abbreviations and acronyms used in the standard. This information corresponds to the Introduction and abbreviations in this handbook.

Clause 5 of the standard provides a description of the architecture and components of an IEEE 802.11 WLAN system. This corresponds to Chapter 2 in this handbook.

Clause 6 of the IEEE 802.11 standard describes the MAC service interface. This is an abstract interface for the exchange of data between the MAC and the protocol layer above the MAC. This is not described explicitly in this handbook.

Clause 7 of the standard describes the MAC frames and their content. Clause 8 of the standard describes the WEP functionality that may be implemented in an IEEE 802.11 station. Clause 9 describes the functionality and frame exchange protocols of the MAC. Information from these clauses is found in Chapter 3.

Clause 10 describes the layer management service interface primitives and their functionality. Clause 11 describes the MAC management functionality and protocols. This information may be found in Chapter 4.

Clause 12 describes the PHY service interface. This is an abstract interface for the exchange of data between the MAC and PHY. Clause 13 describes the PHY management service interface, which consists solely of the MIB interface. This is not described explicitly in this handbook.

Clause 14 describes the frequency hopping spread spectrum physical layer. Clause 15 describes the direct sequence spread spectrum physical layer. Clause 16 describes the infrared baseband physical layer. Clause 17 (IEEE 802.11a) describes the orthogonal frequency division multiplexed physical layer. Clause 18 (IEEE 802.11b) describes the higher rate direct sequence spread spectrum physical layer. Information on all physical layers is found in Chapter 6.

Annex A of the standard is the Protocol Implementation Conformance Statement (PICS) pro forma. This form may be used to identify the exact options implemented in a device claiming conformance to IEEE 802.11. This annex is not discussed in this handbook.

Annex B of the standard is a set of tables of the hopping patterns for the frequency hopping physical layer. This annex is not discussed in this handbook.

Annex C of the standard is the state machine description of the MAC and MAC management functionality. A discussion of the state machines is beyond the scope of this handbook.

Annex D of the standard is the Management Information Base, written in Abstract Syntax Notation 1 (ASN.1) to comply with the requirements of the Simple Network Management Protocol version 2 (SNMPv2). The MAC portion of the MIB is discussed in Chapter 5.

The figure below provides a quick, graphical map between the information in the IEEE 802.11 standard and this handbook.

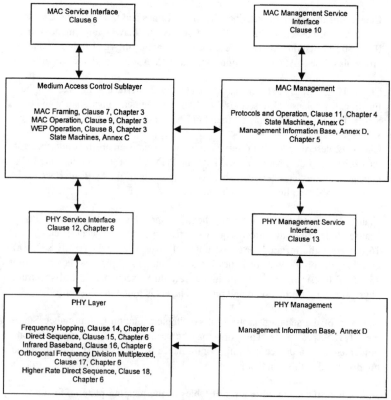

Where to find information on IEEE 802.11

Updated information about IEEE 802.11 and responses to questions by users of this handbook are provided by the authors at the following Web site:
http://www.informed-technology.com/handbook_additional_material.htm.

Contents

The IEEE 802.11 Handbook

A Designer's Companion

Chapter 1
Similarities and Differences between Wireless and Wired LANs

There are many similarities and differences of wired LANs and the IEEE 802.11 wireless LAN (WLAN). This chapter will describe them.

Similarities between WLANs and Wired LANs

From the beginning, the IEEE 802.11 WLAN was designed to look and feel like any IEEE 802 wired LAN. This meant that it must appear to be the same as the wired networks to which a user may be accustomed. It must support all of the protocols and all of the LAN management tools that operate on a wired network.

To accomplish the task of similarity to wired LANs, IEEE 802.11 is designed to the same interface as IEEE 802.3. IEEE 802.11 operates under the IEEE 802.2 logical link control (LLC) sublayer, providing all of the services required supporting that sublayer. In this fashion,

IEEE 802.11 is indistinguishable from IEEE 802.3 by the protocols that may be running above IEEE 802.2.

Using the IEEE 802.2 interface guarantees that protocol layers above LLC need not be aware of the network that is actually transporting their data.

Differences between WLANs and Wired LANs

There are also a number of differences between wired LANs and WLANs. The two most important differences are that there are no wires (the air link) and the mobility thus conferred by the lack of a wired tether. These differences lead to both the tremendous benefits of a WLAN, as well as the perceived drawbacks to them.

The air link is the radio or infrared link between WLAN transmitters and receivers. Because WLAN transmissions are not confined to a wire, there may be concerns that the data carried by a WLAN is not private, not protected. This concern is certainly valid; the data on a WLAN is broadcast for all to hear. Many proprietary WLANs do not provide any protection for the data carried. The designers of IEEE 802.11 realized that this concern could be a significant problem for users wishing to use a WLAN and designed strong cryptographic mechanisms into the protocol to provide protection for the data that is at least as strong as sending the data over a wire. Details of this protection are described in Chapter 3.

The air link also exposes the transmissions of a WLAN to the vagaries of electromagnetic propagation. For both radio- and infrared-based WLANs, everything in the environment is either a reflector or an attenuator of the signal carrying the LAN data. This can cause significant changes in the strength of a signal received by a WLAN station, sometimes severing the station from the LAN entirely. At the wavelengths used in the IEEE 802.11 WLAN, small changes in position can cause large changes in the received signal strength. This is due to the signal traveling many paths of differing length to arrive at the receiver. Each individual arriving signal is of a slightly different phase from all of the others. Adding these different phases together results in the composite signal that is received. Since these individual signals sometimes add up in phase and sometimes out of phase, the overall received signal strength is sometimes large and sometimes small. Objects moving in the environment, such as people, aluminized Mylar balloons, doors, and other objects, can also affect the strength of a signal at a receiver by changing the attenuation or reflection of the many individual signals.

Figure 1-1 is taken from the IEEE Std 802.11-1997 standard and shows the result of a ray tracing simulation in a closed office environment. The various shades of gray depict the different signal strengths at each location in the room. Dealing with the variability of the air link is also designed into the IEEE 802.11 WLAN. For more on this, see Chapter 4.

The second significant difference a WLAN has from a wired LAN is mobility. The user of a WLAN is not tethered to the network outlet in the wall. This is both the source of the benefits of a WLAN and the cause of much of the internal complexity.

The benefit of mobility is that the LAN goes wherever you are, instantly and without the need to search out outlets or to arrange in advance with the network administrators. In a laptop equipped with an IEEE 802.11 WLAN connection, the connection to the network is available in a coworker's office, down the hall in the conference room, downstairs in the lobby, across the parking lot in another building, even across the country on another campus. This means that all of the information available over the network, while sitting in your office, is still available in all these locations: email, file servers, the company-internal web sites, and the Internet.

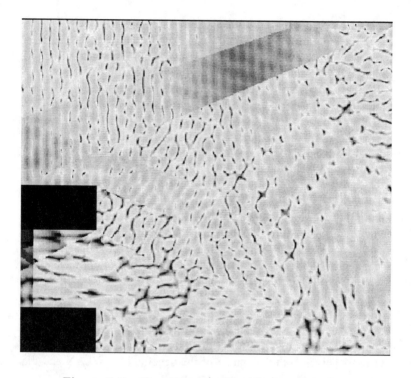

Figure 1-1 — Ray Tracing Simulation Results

Of course, there is a flip side to the benefits of mobility. Most of the network protocols and equipment in use today were not designed to cope with mobility. They were designed with an assumption that the addresses assigned to a network node would remain in a fixed location on the network. For example, early WLANs required that a mobile station could only roam within an area where the WLAN was connected to the wired LAN, with only layer-2 bridges between the parts of the WLAN. This requirement existed because there was no simple way to deal with the change of a layer-3 network address should the mobile station cross from one part of the network to another that is connected by a router. Today, there are ways to deal with this problem using new protocols, including DHCP and Mobile-IP.

Another problem introduced by mobility is that location-based services lose their "hook" to a user's location, when network addresses are not locked to a physical location. Thus, notions such as the nearest network printer must be defined in a different way, when the physical location of a network user may be constantly changing. This may increase the complexity of the service location provider, but meets the needs of the mobile user.

Chapter 2
IEEE Standard 802.11: The First International Standard for WLANs

In 1997 the IEEE adopted the first standard for WLANs, IEEE Std 802.11-1997. This standard was revised in 1999. IEEE Std 802.11-1997 defines a medium access control (MAC) sublayer, MAC management protocols and services, and three physical (PHY) layers. The three PHY layers are an infrared (IR) baseband PHY, a frequency hopping spread spectrum (FHSS) radio in the 2.4 GHz band, and a direct sequence spread spectrum (DSSS) radio in the 2.4 GHz band. All three physical layers describe both 1 and 2 Mbps operation. This chapter will introduce the standard and its concepts.

As this book is being written, the IEEE 802.11 Working Group is developing two new PHY layers. The first, IEEE Std 802.11a, is an orthogonal frequency domain multiplexing (OFDM) radio in the UNII bands, delivering up to 54 Mbps data rates. The second, IEEE Std 802.11b, is an extension to the DSSS PHY in the 2.4 GHz band, delivering up to 11 Mbps data rates.

The goals of the IEEE 802.11 standard is to describe a WLAN that delivers services previously found only in wired networks, e.g., high throughput, highly reliable data delivery, and continuous network connections. In addition, IEEE 802.11 describes a WLAN that allows transparent mobility and built-in power saving operations to the network user. The remainder of this chapter will describe the architecture of the IEEE 802.11 network and the concepts that support that architecture.

IEEE 802.11 Architecture

The architecture of the IEEE 802.11 WLAN is designed to support a network where most decision making is distributed to the mobile stations. This architecture has several advantages, including being very tolerant of faults in all of the WLAN equipment and eliminating any possible bottlenecks a centralized architecture would introduce. The architecture is very flexible, easily supporting both small, transient networks and large semipermanent or permanent networks. In addition, deep power-saving modes of operation are built into the architecture and protocols to prolong the battery life of mobile equipment without losing network connectivity. The IEEE 802.11 architecture comprises several components: the station, the AP, the wireless medium, the basic service set, the DS, and the Extended Service Set. The architecture also includes station services and distribution services.

The IEEE 802.11 architecture may appear to be overly complex. However, this apparent complexity is what provides the IEEE 802.11 WLAN with its robustness and flexibility. The architecture also embeds a level of indirection that has not been present in previous LANs. It is this level of indirection, handled entirely with the IEEE 802.11 architecture and transparent to protocol users of the IEEE 802.11 WLAN, that provides the ability of a mobile station to roam throughout a WLAN and appear to be stationary to the protocols above the MAC that have no concept of mobility. This "sleight of hand" performed by IEEE 802.11 allows all of the existing network protocols to run over a WLAN without any special considerations.

Station

The station is the component that connects to the wireless medium. It consists of a MAC and a PHY. Generally, the station may be referred to as the network adapter or network interface card (NIC). These names may be more familiar to users of wired networks.

The station may be mobile, portable, or stationary. Every station supports station services. These services are authentication, deauthentication, privacy, and delivery of the data (MAC service data unit or MSDU in the standard). The station services will be described below.

Basic Service Set

The IEEE 802.11 WLAN architecture is built around a basic service set (BSS). A BSS is a set of stations that communicate with one another. A BSS does not generally refer to a particular area, due to the uncertainties of electromagnetic propagation. When all of the stations in the BSS are mobile stations and there is no connection to a wired network, the BSS is called an independent BSS (IBSS). The IBSS is the entire network and only those stations communicating with each other in the IBSS are part of the LAN. An IBSS is typically a short-lived network, with a small number of stations, that is created for a particular purpose, e.g., to exchange data with a vendor in the lobby of your company's building or to collaborate on a presentation at a conference.

In an IBSS, the mobile stations all communicate directly with one another. Not every mobile station may be able to communicate with every other mobile station, but they are all part of the same IBSS. There is also no relay function in an IBSS. Thus, if one mobile station must communicate with another, they must be in direct communication range. See Figure 2-1.

Figure 2-1 — Independent Basic Service Set (IBSS)

When a BSS includes an access point (AP), the BSS is no longer independent and is called an infrastructure BSS, but referred to simply as a BSS. An AP is a station that also provides distribution services. Distribution services will be described below.

In an infrastructure BSS, all mobile stations communicate with the AP. The AP provides both the connection to the wired LAN, if any, and the local relay function for the BSS. Thus, if one mobile station in the BSS must communicate with another mobile station, the communication is sent first to the AP and then from the AP to the other mobile station. This causes communications that both originate and end in the same BSS to consume twice the bandwidth that the same communication would consume if sent directly from one mobile station to another. While this appears to be a significant cost, the benefits provided by the AP far outweigh this cost. One of the benefits provided by the AP is the buffering of traffic for a mobile station while that station is operating in a very low power state. The protocols and mechanisms for the support of power saving by mobile stations is described in Chapter 4.

Extended Service Set (ESS)

One of the most desirable benefits of a WLAN is the mobility it provides to its users. This mobility would not be of much use if it were confined to a single BSS. IEEE 802.11 extends the range of mobility it provides to any arbitrary range through the extended service set (ESS). An ESS is a set of infrastructure BSSs, where the APs communicate among themselves to forward traffic from one BSS to another and to facilitate the movement of mobile stations from one BSS to another. The APs perform this communication via an abstract medium called the distribution system (DS). The DS is the backbone of the WLAN and may be constructed of either wired or wireless networks. The DS is a thin layer in each AP that determines if communications received from the BSS are to be relayed back to a destination in the BSS, forwarded on the DS to another AP, or sent into the wired network infrastructure to a destination not in the ESS. Communications received by an AP from the DS are transmitted to the BSS to be received by the destination mobile station. To network equipment outside of the ESS, the ESS and all of its mobile stations appears to be a single MAC-layer network where all stations are physically stationary. Thus, the ESS hides the mobility of the mobile stations from everything outside the ESS. This is the level of indirection provided by the IEEE 802.11 architecture, allowing existing network protocols that have no concept of mobility to operate correctly with a WLAN where there is lots of mobility. See Figure 2-2.

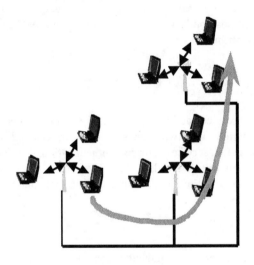

Figure 2-2 — Extended Service Set

One area that is beyond the scope of the IEEE 802.11 standard is the communication between APs. There has been some industry cooperative work in this area to develop an inter-access point protocol (IAPP). Because this work has not yet been completed, it is unlikely that APs from different vendors will communicate well enough to allow a single ESS to be created from APs of different vendors.

Distribution System

The distribution system (DS) is the mechanism by which one AP communicates with another to exchange frames for stations in their BSSs, forward frames to follow mobile stations from one BSS to another, and exchange frames with wired networks, if any. As IEEE 802.11 describes it, the DS is not necessarily a network. The standard does not place any restrictions on how the DS is implemented, only on the services it must provide. Thus, the DS may be a wired network, such as IEEE 802.3, or it may be a purpose-built box that interconnects the APs and provides the required distribution services.

Services

There are nine services defined by the IEEE 802.11 architecture. These services are divided into two groups, station services and distribution services. The station services comprise authentication, deauthentication, privacy, and delivery of the data. The distribution services comprise association, disassociation, reassociation, distribution, and integration.

Station Services

The four station services—authentication, deauthentication, privacy, and data delivery—provide the IEEE 802.11 WLAN similar functions to those that are expected of a wired network. The wired network function of physically connecting to the network cable is similar to the authentication and deauthentication services, where use of the network is allowed only to authorized users. The authentication service is used to prove the identity of one station to another. Without this proof of identity, the station is not allowed to use the WLAN for data delivery. The deauthentication service is used to eliminate a previously authorized user from any further use of the network. Thus, once a station is deauthenticated, e.g., when an employee resigns, that station can no longer access the services of the IEEE 802.11 WLAN.

The privacy service of IEEE 802.11 is designed to provide an equivalent level of protection for data traversing the WLAN as that provided by a wired network that exists in an office building with restricted physical access to the network plant. This service protects the data only as it traverses the wireless medium. It is not designed to provide complete protection of data between applications running over a mixed network environment that happens to include an IEEE 802.11 WLAN.

Finally, the data delivery service of an IEEE 802.11 WLAN is similar to that provided by all other IEEE 802 LANs. The data delivery service provides reliable delivery of data frames from the MAC in one station to the MAC in one or more other stations, with minimal duplication and minimal reordering.

Distribution Services

The five distribution services—association, reassociation, disassociation, distribution, and integration—provide the services necessary to allow mobile stations to roam freely within an ESS and allow an IEEE 802.11 WLAN to connect with the wired LAN infrastructure. The distribution services comprise a thin layer above the MAC and below the LLC sublayer that are invoked to determine how to forward frames within the IEEE 802.11 WLAN and also how to deliver frames from the IEEE 802.11 WLAN to network destinations outside of the WLAN.

The association service is used to make a logical connection between a mobile station and an AP. This logical connection is necessary in order for the DS to know where and how to deliver data to the mobile station. The logical connection is also necessary for the AP to accept data frames from the mobile station and to allocate resources to support the mobile station. Typically, the association service is invoked once, when the mobile station enters the WLAN for the first time, after the application of power or when rediscovering the WLAN after being out of touch for a time.

The reassociation service is similar to the association service, with the exception that it includes information about the AP with which a mobile station has been previously associated. A mobile station will use the reassociation service repeatedly as it moves throughout the ESS, loses contact with the AP with which it is associated, and needs to become associated with a new AP. By using the reassociation service, a mobile station provides information to the AP to which it will be associated that allows that AP to contact the AP with which the mobile station was previously associated, to obtain frames that may be waiting there for delivery to the mobile station, as well as other information that may be relevant.

The disassociation service is used either to force a mobile station to associate or for a mobile station to inform an AP that it no longer requires the services of the WLAN. An AP to inform one or more mobile stations that the AP can no longer provide the logical connection to the WLAN may use the disassociation service. This may be due to demand exceeding available resources in the AP, the AP shutting down, or for any number of other reasons. When the mobile station becomes disassociated, it must begin a new association by invoking the association service.

A mobile station may also use the disassociation service. When a mobile station is aware that it will no longer require the services of the AP, it may invoke the disassociation service to notify the AP that the logical connection to the WLAN from this mobile station is no longer required. For example, this may be done when the mobile station is being shut down or when the IEEE 802.11 adapter card is being ejected. At that point, an AP may free any resources dedicated to the mobile station and recover them for other uses.

An AP to determine how to deliver the frames it receives uses the distribution service. When a mobile station sends a frame to the AP for delivery to another station, the AP invokes the distribution service to determine if the frame should be sent back into its own BSS, for delivery to a mobile station that is associated with the AP, or if the frame should be sent into the DS for delivery to another mobile station associated with a different AP or to a network destination outside the IEEE 802.11 WLAN. The distribution service determines if the frame is sent to another AP or to a portal.

The integration service connects the IEEE 802.11 WLAN to other LANs, including one or more wired LANs, or other IEEE 802.11 WLANs. A portal performs the integration service. The portal is an abstract architectural concept and may physically reside as a thin layer in some or all APs, or may be a separate network component entirely. The integration service translates IEEE 802.11 frames to frames that may traverse another network, and vice versa, translates frames from other networks to frames that may be delivered by an IEEE 802.11 WLAN.

Interaction between Some Services

The IEEE 802.11 standard states that each station must maintain two variables that are dependent on the authentication/deauthentication services and the association/reassociation/disassociation services. The two variables are authentication state and association state. While the standard describes these variables as being enumerated types, they are available only internal to an implementation and can be implemented as Boolean truth-values. The variables are used in a simple state machine that determines the order in which certain services must be invoked and when a station may begin using the data delivery service. The variables must exist in enough instances to allow the station to maintain a unique copy for each station with which it communicates. A station may be authenticated with many different stations simultaneously. However, a station may be associated with only one other station at a time.

A station begins operation in state 1, where both authentication state and association state are false, indicating that the station is neither authenticated nor associated. In state 1, a station may use a very limited number of frame types. (The details of the frame types will be described in Chapter 3.) The allowable frame types provide the capability for a station in state 1 to find an IEEE 802.11 WLAN, an ESS, and its APs, to complete the required frame handshake protocols, and to implement the authentication service. If a station is not successful in becoming authenticated, it will remain in state 1. If a station becomes authenticated, setting authentication state to true, it will make a transition to state 2. See Figure 2-3.

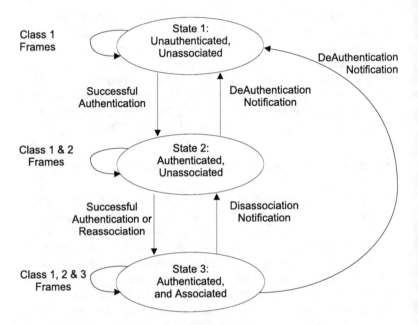

Figure 2-3 — Relationship between State Variables and Services

If a station is part of an IBSS, it is allowed to implement the data service in state 1. This is because neither authentication nor association is used in an IBSS, leaving no mechanism for a station in an IBSS to leave state 1.

In state 2, the station has been authenticated, indicated by authentication state being true, but not yet associated. In this state, additional frame types are allowed, beyond those allowed in state 1. The additional frame types provide the capability for a station in state 2 to implement the association, reassociation, and disassociation services. If a station is not successful in becoming associated, it will remain in state 2, unless it receives a deauthentication notification, in which case it will return to state 1 and authentication state will be made false. If a station becomes associated, setting association state to true, it will make a transition to state 3.

In state 3, the station has been both authenticated and associated, indicated by both authentication state and association state being true. In this state, all frame types are allowed and the station may use the data delivery service. A station will remain in this state until receiving either a disassociation notification or a deauthentication notification, or until it reassociates with another station. If a station receives a disassociation notification, it will make a transition to state 2 and set association state to false. If a station receives a deauthentication notification, it will make a transition to state 1 and set both authentication state and association states to false.

A station must react to frames it receives in each of the states, even those that are disallowed for a particular state. A station will send a deauthentication notification to any station with which it is not authenticated if it receives frames that are not allowed in state 1. A station will send a disassociation notification to any station with which it is authenticated, but not associated, if it receives frames not allowed in state 2. These notifications will force the station that sent the disallowed frames to make a transition to the proper state in the state diagram and allow it to proceed properly toward state 3.

It can now be seen that a station will make transitions between the states of this state machine many times as it roams through an ESS. Because a station may be authenticated with many stations at once, it may be in state 2 with relation to those stations. However, a station may only be in state 3 with relation to a single other station. When a station reassociates with another station, the station with which it was previously associated must be moved back to state 2, by setting the value of associated state for that station to false.

As a graphical example of how the services are used, Figure 2-4 shows a station moving between APs. As the station finds AP1, it will authenticate and associate (a). As the station moves, it may pre-authenticate with AP2 (b). When the station determines that its association with AP1 is no longer desirable, it may reassociate with AP2 (c). The reassociation causes AP2 to notify AP1 of the new location of the station, terminating the station's previous association with AP1 (d). At some point, AP2 may be taken out of service. Should this occur, AP2 would disassociate the stations that were associated with it (e). At this point the station would need to find another access point and authenticate and associate, in order to continue using the wireless LAN (f).

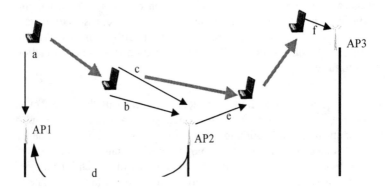

Figure 2-4 — Example Usage of the Services

Summary

The architecture and services of IEEE 802.11 are designed to allow the WLAN to appear identical to wired LANs. The architecture clearly divides the functionality of the WLAN into nonoverlapping functional blocks. The services described by IEEE 802.11 provide the user of IEEE 802.11 with the functionality of a wired LAN and the additional benefits of nearly ubiquitous mobility.

Chapter 3
Medium Access Control

The IEEE 802.11 medium access control (MAC) supplies the functionality required to provide a reliable delivery mechanism for user data over noisy, unreliable wireless media. It does this while also providing advanced LAN services, equal to or beyond those of existing wired LANs.

MAC Functionality

The first function of the MAC is to provide a reliable data delivery service to the users of the MAC. Through a frame exchange protocol at the MAC level, the IEEE 802.11 MAC significantly improves on the reliability of data delivery over wireless media, as compared to earlier WLANs.

The second function of the IEEE 802.11 MAC is to fairly control access to the shared wireless medium. It performs this function through two different access mechanisms: the basic access mechanism, called the distributed coordination function, and a centrally controlled access mechanism, called the point coordination function.

The third function of the IEEE 802.11 MAC is to protect the data that it delivers. Because a WLAN cannot be contained to a particular physical area, in most cases, the IEEE 802.11 MAC provides a privacy service, called Wired Equivalent Privacy (WEP), which encrypts the data sent over the wireless medium. The level of encryption chosen approximates the level of protection data might have on a wired LAN in a building with controlled access that prevents physically connecting to the LAN wiring without authorization.

MAC Frame Exchange Protocol

Because the media used by the IEEE 802.11 WLAN are often very noisy and unreliable, the IEEE 802.11 MAC implements a frame exchange protocol to allow the source of a frame to determine when the frame has been successfully received at the destination. This frame exchange protocol adds some overhead beyond that of other MAC protocols, like IEEE 802.3, because it is not sufficient to simply transmit a frame and expect that the destination has received it correctly on wireless media. In addition, it cannot be expected that every station in a WLAN is able to communicate directly with every other station in the WLAN. This leads to a situation called the hidden node problem. The MAC frame exchange protocol is also designed to address this problem of WLANs. The frame exchange protocol requires the participation of all stations in the WLAN. For this reason, every station decodes and reacts to information in the MAC header of every frame it receives.

Dealing with the Media

The minimal MAC frame exchange protocol consists of two frames, a frame sent from the source to the destination and an acknowledgment from the destination that the frame was received correctly. The frame and its acknowledgment are an atomic unit of the MAC protocol. As such, they cannot be interrupted by the transmission from any other station.

If the source does not receive the acknowledgment, because the destination did not send one due to errors in the original frame or because the acknowledgment itself was corrupted, the source will attempt to transmit the frame again, according to the rules of the basic access mechanism described below. This retransmission of frames by the source effectively reduces the inherent error rate of the medium, at the cost of additional bandwidth consumption. Without this mechanism for retransmission, the users of the MAC, i.e., higher layer protocols, would be left to determine that their packets had been lost through higher layer timeouts or other means. Since higher layer timeouts are often measured in seconds, it is much more efficient to deal with this issue at the MAC layer.

The Hidden Node Problem

A WLAN suffers from a problem that does not occur on a wired LAN. This problem is one of "hidden nodes." It is a result of the fact that every WLAN station cannot be expected to communicate directly with every other WLAN station. An example illustrates this problem most clearly.

In this example, there are three stations, A, B, and C, arranged as shown in Figure 3-1. Station A can communicate only with station B. Station B can communicate with stations A and C. Station C can communicate only with station B. If a simple "transmit and hope" protocol were to be used when station A was sending a frame to station B, the frame could be corrupted by a transmission begun by station C. Station C would be completely unaware of the ongoing transmission from station A to station B.

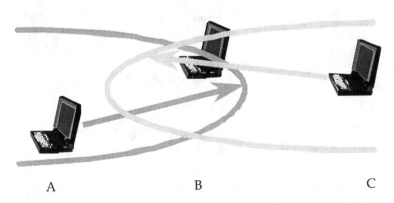

A   B   C

Figure 3-1 — The Hidden Node Problem

The IEEE 802.11 MAC frame exchange protocol addresses this problem by adding two additional frames to the minimal frame exchange protocol described so far. The two frames are a request to send frame and a clear to send frame. The source sends a request to send to the destination. The destination returns a clear to send to the source. Each of these frames contains information that allows other stations receiving them to be notified of the upcoming frame transmission and to delay any transmissions of their own. The request to send and clear to send frames serve to announce to all stations in the neighborhood of both the source and destination the impending transmission from the source to the destination. When the source receives the clear to send from the destination, the real frame that the source wants delivered to the destination is sent. If that frame is correctly received at the destination, the destination will return an acknowledgment, completing the frame exchange protocol. Depending on the configuration of a station and its determination of local conditions, a station may choose when to use the request to send and clear to send frames. See Figure 3-2.

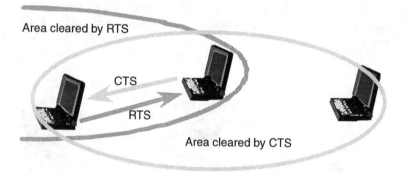

Figure 3-2—RTS and CTS address the Hidden Node Problem

The four frames in this exchange are also an atomic unit of the MAC protocol. They cannot be interrupted by the transmissions of other stations. If this frame exchange fails at any point, the state of the exchange and the information carried in each of the frames allows the stations that have received these frames to recover and regain control of the medium in a minimal amount of time. A station in the neighborhood of the source station receiving the request to send frame will delay any transmissions of its own until it receives the frame announced by the request to send. If the announced frame is not detected, the station may use the medium. Similarly, a station in the neighborhood of the destination station receiving the clear to send frame will delay any transmissions of its own until it receives the acknowledgment frame. If the acknowledgment frame is not detected, the station may use the medium.

In the source station, a failure of the frame exchange protocol causes the frame to be retransmitted. This is treated as a collision, and the rules for scheduling the retransmission are described in the section on the basic access mechanism, below. To prevent the MAC from being monopolized attempting to deliver a single frame, there are retry counters and timers to limit the lifetime of a frame.

While this four-way frame exchange protocol is a required function of the MAC, it may be disabled by an attribute in the management information base (MIB). The value of the dot11RTSThreshold attribute defines the length of a frame that is required to be preceded by the request to send and clear to send frames. All frames of a length greater than the threshold will be sent with the four-way frame exchange. Frames of a length less than or equal to the threshold will not be preceded by the request to send and clear to send. This allows a network designer to tune the operation of the IEEE 802.11 WLAN for the particular environment in which it is deployed. In an environment with low demand for bandwidth or where the stations are concentrated in an area where all are able to hear the transmissions of every station, the threshold may be set so that the request to send and clear to send are never used. As long as stations are not contending with each other, the request to send and clear to send frames will most often be consuming bandwidth for no measurable gain. This is the default setting for the threshold. In an environment where there is a significant demand for the bandwidth available in the WLAN or where the stations are distributed such that some may not hear the transmission of others, the threshold may be set lower, causing long frames to use the request to send and clear to send frame exchange. The value to which the threshold should be set is arrived at by comparing the bandwidth lost to the additional overhead of the protocol to the bandwidth lost from transmissions being corrupted by hidden nodes. A typical value for the threshold is 128. However, the value chosen is dependent on the data rate and should be calculated for the particular data rate in use. It is rarely necessary to change the value of dot11RTSThreshold from the default value in an AP. By definition, an AP is heard by all stations in its BSS and will never be a hidden node. The only situation that may warrant changing the value for the RTS threshold in an AP is when APs are colocated and sharing a channel.

Retry Counters

There are two retry counters associated with every frame the MAC attempts to transmit: a short retry counter and a long retry counter. There is also a lifetime timer associated with every frame the MAC attempts to transmit. Between these counters and the timer, the MAC may determine that it is no longer worthwhile to continue attempting to transmit a particular frame. When the MAC makes that determination, it may cancel the frame's transmission and discard the frame. If a frame is cancelled, the MAC indicates this to the MAC user, through the MAC service interface.

The retry counters limit the number of times a single frame may be retransmitted. There are two counters so that the network designer may choose to allow more or fewer retries to shorter frames, as compared to longer frames. The definition of the length of the frame that uses the short or long counters is determined from the value of an attribute in the MIB, the dot11RTSThreshold. Upon the initial attempt at the transmission of a frame, the retry counters are reset to zero. Frames of a length less than or equal to this threshold will cause the short retry counter to increment when they are retransmitted. Frames of a length greater than the threshold will cause the long retry count to be incremented when they are retransmitted. The successful transmission of a frame will reset the associated retry counter to zero. The attempt to deliver a frame is abandoned if either retry counter reaches the limit with which it is associated in the MIB. The short retry counter is associated with the dot11ShortRetryLimit attribute. The long retry counter is associated with the dot11LongRetryLimit attribute.

Basic Access Mechanism

The basic access mechanism is carrier sense multiple access with collision avoidance (CSMA/CA) with binary exponential backoff. This access mechanism is similar to that used in IEEE 802.3, with some significant exceptions. CSMA/CA is a "listen before talk" (LBT) access mechanism. In this type of access mechanism, a station will listen to the medium before beginning a transmission. If the medium is already carrying a transmission, the station that is listening will not begin its own transmission. This is the CSMA portion of the access mechanism. This is implemented, in part, using a physical carrier sensing mechanism provided by the PHY. Had the listening station begun its transmission while the medium was already carrying another transmission, a collision would occur on the medium. The collision may cause one or both of the transmissions to be corrupted to the extent that the transmissions could not be correctly received. Thus, the operation of the access mechanism works to ensure the correct reception of the information transmitted on the wireless medium.

As IEEE 802.11 implements this access mechanism, when a station listens to the medium before beginning its own transmission and detects an existing transmission in progress, the listening station enters a deferral period determined by the binary exponential backoff algorithm. It will also increment the appropriate retry counter associated with the frame. The binary exponential backoff mechanism chooses a random number which represents the amount of time that must elapse while there are not any transmissions, i.e., the medium is idle before the listening station may attempt to begin its transmission again. The random number resulting from this algorithm is uniformly distributed in a range, called the contention window, the size of which doubles with every attempt to transmit that is deferred, until a maximum size is reached for the range. Once a transmission is successfully transmitted, the range is reduced to its minimum value for the next transmission. Both the minimum and maximum values for the contention window range are fixed for a particular PHY. However, the values may differ from one PHY to another.

Because it is extremely unusual for a wireless device to be able to receive and transmit simultaneously, the IEEE 802.11 MAC uses collision avoidance rather than the collision detection of IEEE 802.3. It is also unusual for all wireless devices in a LAN to be able to communicate directly with all other devices. For this reason, the IEEE 802.11 MAC implements a network allocation vector (NAV). The NAV is a value that indicates to a station the amount of time that remains before the medium will become available. The NAV is kept current through duration values that are transmitted in all frames. By examining the NAV, a station may avoid transmitting, even when the medium does not appear to be carrying a transmission by the physical carrier sense. The NAV, then, is a virtual carrier sensing mechanism. By combining the virtual carrier sensing mechanism with the physical carrier sensing mechanism, the MAC implements the collision avoidance portion of the CSMA/CA access mechanism.

Timing Intervals

The decision by a station that the medium is not carrying a transmission when the station is listening before beginning its own transmission is based on timing intervals. The IEEE 802.11 MAC recognizes five timing intervals. There are two basic intervals determined by the PHY: the short interframe space (SIFS) and the slot time. Three additional intervals are built from the two basic intervals: the priority interframe space (PIFS), the distributed interframe space (DIFS), and the extended interframe space (EIFS). The SIFS is the shortest interval, followed by the slot time, which is slightly longer. The PIFS is equal to SIFS plus one slot time. The

DIFS is equal to the SIFS plus two slot times. The EIFS is much larger than any of the other intervals. It is used when a frame that contains errors is received by the MAC, allowing the possibility for the MAC frame exchanges to complete correctly before another transmission is allowed. Through these five timing intervals, both the distributed coordination function (DCF) and point coordination function (PCF) are implemented.

DCF Operation

The DCF operates as follows. When the MAC receives a request to transmit a frame, a check is made of the physical and virtual carrier sense mechanisms. If both mechanisms indicate that the medium is not in use for an interval of DIFS (or EIFS if the previously received frame contained errors), the MAC may begin transmission to the frame. If either the physical or virtual carrier sense mechanisms indicate that the medius is in use during the DIFS interval, the MAC will select a backoff interval using the binary exponential backoff mechanism and increment the appropriate retry counter. The MAC will decrement the backoff value each time the medium is detected to be idle by both the physical and virtual carrier sense mechanisms for an interval of one slot time. Once the backoff interval has expired, the MAC begins the transmission. If the transmission is not successful, i.e., the acknowledgment is not received, a collision is considered to have occurred. In this case, the contention window is doubled, a new backoff interval is selected, and the backoff countdown is begun, again. This process will continue until the transmission is sent successfully or it is cancelled. See Figure 3-3.

Centrally Controlled Access Mechanism

The centrally controlled access mechanism uses a poll and response protocol to eliminate the possibility of contention for the medium. This access mechanism is called the point coordination function (PCF). A point coordinator (PC) controls the PCF. The PC is always located in an AP. Generally, the PCF operates by stations requesting that the PC register them on a polling list, and the PC then regularly polls the

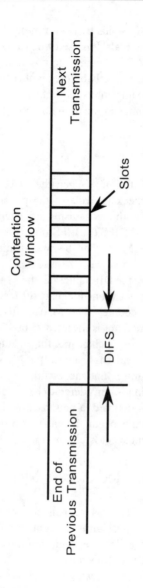

Figure 3-3 — DCF Timing

stations for traffic while also delivering traffic to the stations. With proper planning, the PCF is able to deliver a near-isochronous service to the stations on the polling list. The PCF is built over the DCF and both operate simultaneously. While the PCF is an optional part of the IEEE 802.11 standard, every station is required to be able to respond to the operation of the PCF.

The PCF makes use of the PIFS, which is shorter than the DIFS, to seize and maintain control of the medium. The PC begins a period of operation called the contention-free period (CFP), during which the PCF is operating. This period is called contention free because access to the medium is completely controlled by the PC and the DCF is prevented from gaining access to the medium. The CFP occurs periodically to provide a near-isochronous service to the stations. The CFP also alternates with a contention period where the normal DCF rules operate and all stations may compete for access to the medium. The standard requires that the contention period be long enough to contain at least one maximum length frame and its acknowledgment.

The CFP begins when the PC gains access to the medium, using the normal DCF procedures, and transmits a Beacon frame (described later in this chapter). Beacon frames are required to be transmitted periodically also. Because the PC must compete for the medium, the beginning of the CFP may be delayed from its ideal start time. Once the PC has control of the medium, it begins to deliver traffic to stations in its BSS and may poll stations that have requested contention-free service for them to deliver traffic to the PC. Thus, the traffic in the CFP will consist of frames sent from the PC to one or more stations, followed by the acknowledgment from those stations. Every IEEE 802.11 station is capable of receiving frames addressed to it from the PC during the CFP and returning an acknowledgment. In addition, the PC sends a contention-free poll (CF-Poll) frame to those stations that have requested contention-free service. If the station polled has traffic to send, it may transmit one frame for each CF-Poll received. If the station does not have traffic to send, it does not respond to the poll. The ability to respond to the CF-Poll frame is an option in the standard.

In order to make the use of the medium more efficient during the CFP, it is possible to piggyback both the acknowledgment and the CF-Poll onto data frames. Thus, a frame sent to a station from the PC may include a CF-Poll of that station for it to send traffic back to the PC. The frame sent from the station to the PC may include the acknowledgment of the frame just received from the PC. The PC may combine both the CF-Poll and the acknowledgment with a data frame, as well. In this last case, the PC may be sending a frame to one station, along with a CF-Poll, and acknowledging a frame received from an entirely different station.

During the CFP, the PC ensures that the interval between frames on the medium is no longer than PIFS. This is done to prevent a station operating under the DCF from gaining access to the medium. The PC will send a frame to a station and expect the responding frame, either an acknowledgment or a data frame in response to a CF-Poll, within a SIFS interval. If the response is not received before that SIFS interval expires, the PC will transmit its next frame before a PIFS interval expires after the previous transmission. This will continue until the CFP is concluded. This operation of the PC is actually a secondary mechanism to prevent access by the stations until the CFP is concluded. Another mechanism also keeps the stations off the medium during the CFP.

The primary mechanism used to prevent stations from accessing the medium during the CFP is the NAV. The Beacon that is sent by the PC at the beginning of the CFP contains information from the PC about the maximum expected length of the CFP. Every station receiving the Beacon will enter this information into its NAV and thus, be prevented from independently accessing the medium until the CFP concludes. The use of the PIFS interval, described above, is a backup mechanism used to prevent stations that did not receive the Beacon from accessing the medium.

Because the CFP is not a true isochronous service, where the total bandwidth demand and thus, the time of transmission is know precisely in advance, the PC announces the end of the CFP by transmitting a contention-free end (CF-End) frame. This frame is the formal conclusion of the CFP. It causes the stations that had set their NAVs from the initial Beacon frame to reset the NAV. Once the NAV is reset, the stations are able to begin the operation of the DCF, independently competing for access to the medium. Like the acknowledgment and CF-Poll during the CFP, the CF-End may also be combined with an acknowledgment of a data transmission from a mobile station. See Figure 3-4.

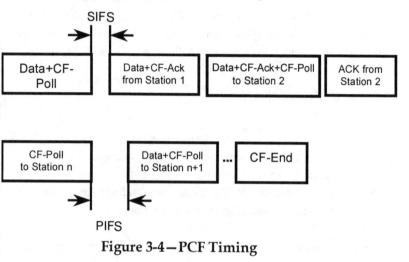

Figure 3-4—PCF Timing

Frame Formats

The IEEE 802.11 MAC accepts MSDUs from higher layers in the protocol stack for the purpose of reliably sending those MSDUs to the equivalent layer of the protocol stack in another station. To accomplish this task, the MAC adds information to the MSDU in the form of headers and trailers to create a MAC protocol data unit (MPDU). The MPDU is then passed to the physical layer to be sent over the wireless medium to the other stations. In addition, the MAC may fragment MSDUs into several frames, increasing the probability of each individual frame being delivered successfully. A discussion of fragmentation follows the description of frame formats in this chapter.

The header and trailer information, combined with the information received as the MSDU, is referred to as the MAC frame. This frame contains, among other things, addressing information, IEEE 802.11-specific protocol information, information for setting the NAV, and a frame check sequence for verifying the integrity of the frame. The details of the frame format are presented in the following sections.

General Frame Format

The general IEEE 802.11 frame format is shown in Figure 3-5. This frame format is quite a bit more complex than that for most other LAN protocols. During the development of the standard, much discussion surrounded the frame format. The format that resulted is considered the best design balancing both efficiency and functionality.

The frame begins with a MAC header. The start of the header is the frame control field. A field that contains the duration information for the NAV or a short identifier follows it. Three addressing fields follow that field. The next field contains frame sequence information. The final field of the MAC header is the fourth address field. It appears that the MAC header is very long; however, not all of these fields are used in all frames.

Following the MAC header is the frame body. The frame body contains the MSDU from the higher layer protocols. The final field in the MAC frame is the frame check sequence.

Each of these fields will be described. Following that, the use of the fields in particular frame types will be discussed.

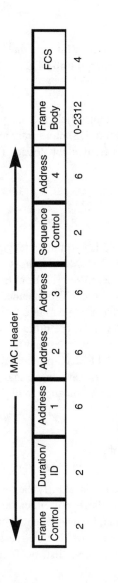

Figure 3-5 — IEEE 802.11 Frame Format

Frame Control Field

The frame control field is a sixteen-bit field that comprises the information the MAC requires to interpret all of the subsequent fields of the MAC header.

The subfields of the frame control field are: the protocol version, frame type and subtype, To DS, From DS, more fragments, retry, power management, more data, Wired Equivalent Privacy (WEP), and order. See Figure 3-6.

Protocol Version

The protocol version subfield is two bits in length. It is used to identify the version of the IEEE 802.11 MAC protocol used to construct the frame. This version field is set to zero in the current version of the standard. All other values are reserved. The intended operation of this subfield is to allow a station receiving a frame to determine if the frame was constructed with a version of the protocol that the station understands. If the protocol version indicates that the frame was constructed by a version of the IEEE 802.11 MAC protocol that the station does not understand, the station must discard the frame and not generate any response on the medium or any indication to higher layer protocols that the frame was received.

Frame Type and Subtype

The frame type and subtype fields identify the function of the frame and which other MAC header fields are present in the frame. There are three frame types: control, data, and management. The fourth frame type is currently reserved. Within each frame type there are several subtypes. Table 3-1 provides the complete list of frame type and subtype combinations.

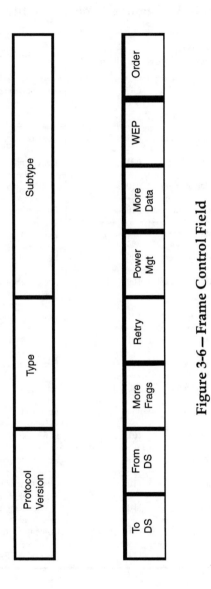

Figure 3-6 — Frame Control Field

Table 3-1 — Frame Type and Subtype

Type value b3 b2	Type description	Subtype value b7 b6 b5 b4	Subtype description
00	Management	0000	Association request
00	Management	0001	Association response
00	Management	0010	Reassociation request
00	Management	0011	Reassociation response
00	Management	0100	Probe request
00	Management	0101	Probe response
00	Management	0110-0111	Reserved
00	Management	1000	Beacon
00	Management	1001	Announcement traffic indication message (ATIM)
00	Management	1010	Disassociation
00	Management	1011	Authentication
00	Management	1100	Deauthentication
00	Management	1101–1111	Reserved
01	Control	0000–1001	Reserved
01	Control	1010	Power save (PS)-poll
01	Control	1011	Request to send (RTS)
01	Control	1100	Clear to send (CTS)
01	Control	1101	Acknowledgment (ACK)
01	Control	1110	Contention free (CF)-End
01	Control	1111	CF-End + CF-ACK

Table 3-1 — Frame Type and Subtype (*Continued*)

Type value b3 b2	Type description	Subtype value b7 b6 b5 b4	Subtype description
10	Data	0000	Data
10	Data	0001	Data + CF-ACK
10	Data	0010	Data + CF-Poll
10	Data	0011	Data + CF-ACK + CF-Poll
10	Data	0100	Null function (no data)
10	Data	0101	CF-ACK (no data)
10	Data	0110	CF-Poll (no data)
10	Data	0111	CF-ACK + CF-Poll (no data)
10	Data	1000–1111	Reserved
11	Reserved	0000–1111	Reserved

To DS and From DS Subfields

The To DS subfield is a single bit in length. It is used only in data type frames to indicate that the frame is destined for the DS. It will be set in every data frame sent from a mobile station to the AP. This bit is zero in all other types of frames.

The From DS subfield is a single bit in length. It is also used only in data type frames to indicate that the frame is being sent from the DS. This bit will be set in every data frame sent from the AP to a mobile station. This bit is zero in all other types of frames.

There are four allowable combinations for these two subfields. When both subfields are zero, the frame is a direct communication between two mobile stations. When the To DS subfield is one and the From DS subfield is zero, the frame is a transmission from a mobile station to an

AP. When the To DS subfield is zero and the From DS subfield is one, the frame is a transmission from an AP to a mobile station. The final combination, when both subfields are one, is used for a special case where an IEEE 802.11 WLAN is being used as the DS. This last case is referred to as a wireless DS.

The reason for the special case of a wireless DS is to allow the DS to occupy the same medium as the BSS. If this case did not exist, there could be confusion about the addressing of the frames. When both subfields are one, the frame is being sent (distributed) from one AP to another, over the wireless medium.

More Fragments Subfield

The more fragments subfield is a single bit in length. This subfield is used to indicate that this frame is not the last fragment of a data or management frame that has been fragmented. This subfield is zero in the last fragment of a data or management frame that has been fragmented, in all control frames, and in any data or management frame that is not fragmented.

Retry Subfield

This subfield is a single bit in length. It is used to indicate whether a data or management frame is being transmitted for the first time or if it is a retransmission. When this subfield is zero, the frame is being sent for the first time. When this subfield is one, the frame is a retransmission. The receiving MAC, to enable it to filter out duplicate received frames, uses this subfield, along with the sequence number subfield.

Power Management Subfield

This subfield is a single bit in length. A mobile station uses the power management subfield to announce its power management state. The value of the subfield indicates the power management state that the station will enter when a successful frame exchange is completed. A zero in this subfield indicates that the station is in the active mode and will be available for future communication. A one in this subfield indicates that the station will be entering the power management mode and will not be available for future communication. This subfield must contain the same value for all frames transmitted by the station during a single frame exchange. The station may not change its power management state until it has completed a successful frame exchange. A successful frame exchange is the complete two-way or four-way frame handshake, including the correct reception of an acknowledgment.

More Data Subfield

The more data subfield is a single bit in length. The AP uses this subfield to indicate to a mobile station that there is at least one frame buffered at the AP for the mobile station. When this subfield is one, there is at least one frame buffered at the AP for the mobile station. When this subfield is zero, there are no frames buffered at the AP for the mobile station. A mobile station that is polled by the PC during a CFP also may use this subfield to indicate to the PC that there is at least one more frame buffered at the mobile station to be sent to the PC. In multicast frames, the AP may also set this subfield to one to indicate that there are more multicast frames buffered at the AP.

WEP Subfield

The WEP subfield is a single bit in length. When set to one, it indicates that the frame body of the MAC frame has been encrypted using the WEP algorithm. This subfield may be set to one only in data frames and management frames of subtype authentication. It is zero in all other frame types and subtypes.

Order Subfield

This subfield is a single bit in length. When set to one, this subfield indicates that the content of the data frame was provided to the MAC with a request for strictly ordered service. This subfield provides information to the AP and DS to allow this service to be delivered.

Duration/ID Field

The duration/ID field is 16 bits in length. It alternately contains duration information for updating the NAV or a short ID, called the association ID (AID), used by a mobile station to retrieve frames that are buffered for it at the AP. Only the power-save poll (PS-Poll) frame contains the AID. In that frame, the AID is aligned in the least significant 14 bits of the field. The most significant two bits of the field are both set to one in the PS-Poll frame. Because of other limitations in the protocol, the maximum allowable value for the AID is 2007. All values larger than 2007 are reserved.

When bit 15 of the field is zero, the value in bits 14-0 represent the remaining duration of a frame exchange. This value is used to update the NAV, preventing a station receiving this field from beginning a transmission that might cause corruption of the ongoing transmission.

The value of the duration/ID field is set to 32, 768 (i.e., bit 15 is one and all other bits are zero) in all frames transmitted during the CFP. This value is chosen to allow a station that did not receive the beginning of the CFP to recognize that a CFP is ongoing and to set its NAV to a value large enough not to interfere with the CFP.

Other than the AID values, where bits 15 and 14 are set to one, all other values in this field are reserved.

Address Fields

The MAC frame format contains four address fields. Any particular frame type may contain one, two, three, or four address fields. In IEEE Std 802.11-1997, the address format is the familiar IEEE 48-bit address, normally used to identify the source and destination MAC addresses contained in a frame, as in IEEE 802.3. In addition to the source address (SA) and destination address (DA), IEEE Std 802.11-1997 defines three additional address types: the transmitter address (TA), the receiver address (RA), and the BSS identifier (BSSID). These additional address types are used in IEEE Std 802.11-1997 to facilitate the level of indirection of IEEE Std 802.11-1997 that allows transparent mobility and to provide a mechanism for filtering multicast frames. The position of the address in the address fields determines its function.

An IEEE 48-bit address comprises three fields: a single-bit Individual/Group field, a single-bit Universal/Local field, and a 46-bit address field. The Individual/Group field defines whether the address is that of a single MAC or of a group of MACs. When the Individual/Group field is set to one, the remainder of the address is that of a group. If, in addition, all of the remaining bits in the address are set to one, the group is the broadcast group and includes all stations. When the Individual/Group bit is zero, the remainder of the address identifies a single MAC. The Universal/Local field defines whether the address is administered globally by the IEEE or locally. When the Universal/Local field is zero, the address is a globally administered address and should be unique. When the Universal/Local field is set to one, the address is locally administered and may not be unique.

BSS Identifier

The BSS Identifier (BSSID) is a unique identifier for a particular BSS of an IEEE 802.11 WLAN. Its format is identical to that of an IEEE 48-bit address. In an infrastructure BSS, the BSSID is the MAC address of the AP. Using the MAC address of the AP for the BSSID ensures that the BSSID will be unique and also simplifies the address processing in the AP. In an independent BSS, the BSSID is a locally administered, individual address that is generated randomly by the station that starts the IBSS. The generation of this address from a random number provides some assurance that the address will be unique. However, there is a finite probability that the address generated is not unique. In both infrastructure and independent BSSs, the BSSID must be an individual address. There is only one case where a group address is used. That is in a probe request frame. The use of the BSSID in the probe request frame will be discussed in the description of that frame type.

Transmitter Address

The transmitter address (TA) is the address of the MAC that transmitted the frame onto the wireless medium. This address is always an individual address. The TA is used by stations receiving a frame to identify the station to which any responses in the MAC frame exchange protocol will be sent.

Receiver Address

The receiver address (RA) is the address of the MAC to which the frame is sent over the wireless medium. This address may be either an individual or group address.

Source Address

The source address (SA) is the address of the MAC that originated the frame. This address is always an individual address. This address does not always match the address in the TA field because of the indirection that is performed by the DS of an IEEE 802.1 WLAN. It is the SA field that should be used to identify the source of a frame when indicating a frame has been received to higher layer protocols.

Destination Address

The destination address (DA) is the address of the final destination to which the frame is sent. This address may be either an individual or group address. This address does not always match the address in the RA field because of the indirection that is performed by the DS.

Sequence Control Field

The sequence control field is a 16-bit field comprising two subfields. The subfields are a 4-bit fragment number and a 12-bit sequence number. As a whole, this field is used to allow a receiving station to eliminate duplicate received frames.

Sequence Number Subfield

The sequence number subfield contains a 12-bit number assigned sequentially by the sending station to each MSDU. This sequence number is incremented after each assignment and wraps back to zero when incremented from 4095. The sequence number for a particular MSDU is transmitted in every data frame associated with the MSDU. It is constant over all transmissions and retransmissions of the MSDU. If the MSDU is fragmented, the sequence number of the MSDU is sent with each frame containing a fragment of the MSDU.

Fragment Number Subfield

The fragment number subfield contains a 4-bit number assigned to each fragment of an MSDU. The first, or only, fragment of an MSDU is assigned a fragment number of zero. Each successive fragment is assigned a sequentially incremented fragment number. The fragment number is constant in all transmissions or retransmissions of a particular fragment.

Frame Body Field

The frame body field contains the information specific to the particular data or management frames. This field is variable length. It may be as long as 2304 bytes, without WEP encryption, or 2312 bytes, when the frame body is encrypted using WEP. The value of 2304 bytes as the maximum length of this field was chosen to allow an application to send 2048-byte pieces of information, which can then be encapsulated by as many as 256 bytes of upper layer protocol headers and trailers.

Frame Check Sequence Field

The frame check sequence field is 32 bits in length. It contains the result of applying the CCITT CRC-32 polynomial to the MAC header and frame body. The CRC-32 polynomial is represented by the following equation:

$$G(x) = x^{32} + x^{26} + x^{23} + x^{22} + x^{16} + x^{12} + x^{11} + x^{10} + x^8 + x^7 + x^5 + x^4 + x^2 + x + 1$$

This is the same polynomial used in other IEEE 802 LAN standards. The frame check sequence in an IEEE 802.11 frame is generated in the same way as it is in IEEE 802.3.

Control Frame Subtypes

There are six control frame subtypes: request to send (RTS), clear to send (CTS), acknowledge (ACK), power save poll (PS-Poll), contention-free end (CF-End), and contention-free end plus ACK (CF-End+ACK). A description of these frames follows.

Request to Send

The request to send (RTS) frame is 20 bytes in length. It comprises the frame control field, the duration/ID field, two address fields and the frame check sequence field. The purpose of this frame is to transmit the duration information to those stations in the neighborhood of the transmitter, in order that the stations receiving the RTS frame will update their NAV to prevent transmissions from colliding with the data or management frame that is expected to follow. The RTS is also the first frame in a four-way frame exchange handshake between the transmitter and the receiver. See Figure 3-7.

The RA identifies the individual MAC that is the immediate intended recipient of the frame. In an RTS frame, the RA is always an individual

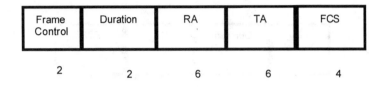

Frame Control	Duration	RA	TA	FCS
2	2	6	6	4

Figure 3-7—Request to Send Frame

address. The TA identifies the source of the transmission. It is used by the station addressed by the RA to form the clear to send (CTS) frame that is the response to the RTS. The duration information conveyed by this frame is a measure of the amount of time required to complete the four-way frame exchange. The value of the duration is the length of time to transmit a CTS, the data or management frame, the acknowledge (ACK) frame, and the two SIFS intervals between the CTS and the data or management frame and between the data or management frame and the ACK. The duration is measured in microseconds. Fractional microseconds are always rounded up to the next larger integer value.

Clear to Send

The clear to send (CTS) frame is 14 bytes in length. It comprises the frame control field, the duration/ID field, one address field and the frame check sequence field. The purpose of this frame is to transmit the duration information to those stations in the neighborhood of the station intended to receive the expected data or management frame, in order that the stations receiving the CTS frame will update their NAV to prevent transmissions from colliding with the data or management frame that is expected to follow. The CTS is the second frame in a four-way frame exchange handshake between the transmitter and the receiver. See Figure 3-8.

The RA identifies the individual MAC address of the station to which the CTS is sent. In the CTS frame, the RA is always an individual address.

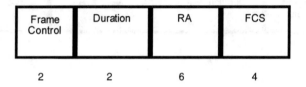

Frame Control	Duration	RA	FCS
2	2	6	4

Figure 3-8 — Clear to Send Frame

The RA value is taken directly from the TA of the preceding RTS frame. The duration information conveyed by this frame is a measure of the time required to complete the four-way frame exchange handshake. The value of the duration is the length of time to send the subsequent data or management frame, the acknowledge frame, and one SIFS interval. The duration value is calculated by subtracting the length of time to transmit a CTS and one SIFS interval from the duration that was received in the RTS frame. The duration is measured in microseconds. Fractional microseconds are always rounded up to the next larger integer value.

Acknowledge

The acknowledge (ACK) frame is 14 bytes in length. It comprises the frame control field, the duration/ID field, on address field and the frame check sequence field. The purpose of this frame is two-fold. First, the ACK frame transmits an acknowledgment to the sender of the immediately previous data, management, or PS-Poll frame that the frame was received correctly. This informs the sender of the frame of the frame's receipt and eliminates the requirement for retransmission by the sender. Second, the ACK frame is used to transmit the duration information for a fragment burst to those stations in the neighborhood of the station intended to receive the fragments. In this case, it performs exactly as the CTS frame. The ACK frame is the fourth frame in the four-way frame exchange handshake between transmitter and receiver. See Figure 3-9.

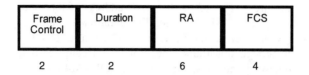

Frame Control	Duration	RA	FCS
2	2	6	4

Figure 3-9 — Acknowledge (ACK) Frame

The RA identifies the individual MAC address of the station to which the ACK is sent. In the ACK frame, the RA is always an individual address. The RA value is taken directly from the address 2 field of the immediately preceding data, management, or PS-Poll frame.

The value of the duration information is zero, if the ACK is an acknowledgment of a PS-Poll frame or is an acknowledgment of a management or data frame where the more fragments subfield of the frame control field is zero. The value of the duration information is the time to transmit the subsequent data or management frame, an ACK frame, and two SIFS intervals, if the acknowledgment is of a data or management frame where the more fragments subfield of the frame control field is one. In the latter case, the duration may be calculated by subtracting the length of time to transmit the ACK frame and one SIFS interval from the duration value received in the immediately preceding data or management frame. The duration value is measured in microseconds. Fractional microseconds are always rounded up to the next integer value.

Power Save Poll

The power save poll (PS-Poll) frame is 20 bytes in length. It comprises the frame control field, the duration/ID field, two address fields, and the frame check sequence field. The purpose of this frame is to request that an AP deliver a frame that has been buffered for a mobile station while it was in a power saving mode.

The BSSID identifies the AP to which this frame is directed. This BSSID should be the same BSSID as that to which the sending station has previously associated. The BSSID in the PS-Poll frame is always an individual address. The TA is the MAC address of the mobile station that is sending the PS-Poll frame. The duration/ID value is the AID value that was given to the mobile station upon association with the BSS. Even though this frame does not include any explicit duration information, every mobile station receiving a PS-Poll frame will update its NAV with a value which is the length of time to transmit an ACK frame and a single SIFS interval. This action allows the ACK frame that follows the PS-Poll to be sent by the AP with a very small probability that it will collide with frames from mobile stations.

For the AP response to this frame, see Chapter 4.

CF-End and CF-End+ACK

The CF-End and CF-End+ACK frames are 20 bytes in length. Each frame comprises the frame control field, the duration/ID field, two address fields, and the frame check sequence field. The purpose of these frames is to conclude a CFP and to release stations from the restriction imposed during a CFP, preventing competition for access to the medium. Additionally, the CF-End+ACK frame is used to acknowledge the last transmission received by the PC. This frame is sent by the PC as the last frame in the CFP.

The RA is the broadcast group address, as this frame is intended to be received by every station in the BSS. The BSSID is the MAC address of the AP, where the PC resides. The duration value is zero, ensuring that the NAVs of all stations receiving this frame will be reset to zero.

Data Frame Subtypes

There are eight data frame subtypes in two groups. The first group is simple data, data with contention-free acknoweldgment (CF-ACK), data with CF-Poll, and data with CF-ACK and CF-Poll. The second group is null function, CF-ACK, CF-Poll, and CF-ACK+CF-Poll. The first group of data frames actually carry a nonzero number of data bytes. The second group of data frames carry no data bytes at all.

The data frame is variable in length. The minimum length of the data frame is 29 bytes. The maximum length of the frame is 2346 bytes. The data frame carries the MSDU requested to be delivered by the upper layer protocols. It comprises the frame control field, the duration/ID field, up to four address fields, the sequence control field, the frame body field and the frame check sequence field. See Figure 3-10.

Data

The simple data frame encapsulates the upper layer protocol packets, delivering them from one IEEE 802.11 station to another. It may appear in both the contention period and contention-free period.

The duration/ID field contains a value, measured in microseconds from the end of the data frame, sufficient to protect the transmission of a subsequent acknowledgment frame. If the data frame is sent to a multicast address, the duration/ID value is zero.

The use of the four address fields in the data frame are dependent on two things, whether the BSS to which the transmitting station belongs is an independent BSS or an infrastructure BSS, and whether the transmitting and/or receiving stations are part of the DS. Table 3-2 identifies the functions of each of the address fields for the four possible cases of the To DS and From DS bits.

The address 1 field is always used to perform receive address matching decisions. If the address in the address 1 field is an individual address, the station will receive the frame and indicate it to higher layer protocols only if the address matches its own. When the address 1 field contains a group address, the BSSID is also checked to determine that the frame was sent from a station in the same BSS to which the receiving station belongs.

Frame Control	Duration/ ID	Address 1	Address 2	Address 3	Sequence Control	Address 4	Frame Body	FCS
2	2	6	6	6	2	6	0-2312	4

Figure 3-10—Data Frame

Table 3-2 — Address Field Functions

Function	To DS	From DS	Address 1	Address 2	Address 3	Address 4
IBSS	0	0	RA = DA	SA	BSSID	N/A
From the AP	0	1	RA = DA	BSSID	SA	N/A
To the AP	1	0	RA = BSSID	SA	DA	N/A
Wireless DS	1	1	RA	TA	DA	SA

The address 2 field is used to identify the sender of the frame. The content of this field is used to direct any required acknowledgment back to the sender. This address is always an individual address.

The address 3 field carries additional information for frame filtering or forwarding by the DS. A frame received by a mobile station from an AP will use the address in this field to indicate the source address of the frame to higher layer protocols. A frame received by an AP from a mobile station will use the address in this field as the destination address of the frame for DS forwarding decisions. In the case of the wireless DS, this field contains the destination address of the frame that was originally received by the AP.

The address 4 field is used only in a wireless DS as one AP forwards a frame to another AP. This field is not present in any other data frame. In this case the source address from the original frame received by the AP is contained in this field. The address in this field will be placed by the DS into the address 3 field of a frame that is delivered by the AP to a mobile station, or into the SA of a frame that is passed onto a wired network.

The DA is the destination of the MSDU in the frame body field. The SA is the address of the MAC entity that initiated the MSDU in the frame body field. The RA is the address of the station contained in the AP in the wireless DS that is the next immediate intended recipient of the frame. The TA is the address of the station contained in the AP in the wireless DS that is transmitting the frame. The BSSID of the data frame is determined as follows:

a)   If the station is an AP or is associated with an AP, the BSSID is the address currently in use by the station contained in the AP.

b)   If the station is a member of an IBSS, the BSSID is the BSSID of the IBSS.

Data + CF-ACK

The Data + CF-ACK frame is identical to the simple data frame, with the following exceptions. The Data + CF-ACK frame may be sent only during a CFP. It is never used in an IBSS. The acknowledgment carried in this frame is acknowledging the previously received data frame, which may not be associated with the address of the destination of the current frame.

Data + CF-Poll

The Data + CF-Poll frame is identical to the simple data frame, with the following exceptions. The Data + CF-Poll frame may be sent only by the PC during a CFP. This frame is never sent by a mobile station. It is never used in an IBSS. This frame is used by the PC to deliver data to a mobile station and simultaneously request that the mobile station send a data frame that it may have buffered, when the current reception is completed.

Data + CF-ACK + CF-Poll

The Data + CF-ACK + CF-Poll frame is identical to the simple data frame, with the following exceptions. The Data + CF-ACK + CF-Poll frame may be sent only by the PC during a CFP. This frame is never sent by a mobile station. It is never used in an IBSS. This frame combines the functions of both the Data + CF-ACK and Data + CF-Poll frames into a single frame.

Null Function (no data)

The null function frame, a data frame that contains no frame body and thus no data, is used to allow a station that has nothing to transmit to be able to complete the frame exchange necessary for changing its power management state. The sole purpose for this frame is to carry the power management bit in the frame control field to the AP, when a station changes to a low power operating state. More detail on power management operation is provided in Chapter 4.

CF-ACK (no data)

The CF-ACK frame may be used by a mobile station that has received a data frame from the PC during the CFP to acknowledge the correct receipt of that frame. Because this frame is 29 bytes long, it is more efficient to use an acknowledgment control frame (ACK frame). Either frame will provide the required acknowledgment to the PC.

CF-Poll (no data)

The CF-Poll frame is used by the PC to request that a mobile station send a pending data frame during the CFP. The PC will send this frame, rather than the Data + CF-Poll, when it has no data to be sent to the mobile station.

CF-ACK + CF-Poll (no data)

The CF-ACK + CF-Poll is used by the PC to acknowledge a correctly received frame and to solicit a pending frame from a mobile station. The acknowledgment and the solicitation may be intended for disparate mobile stations.

Management Frame Subtypes

IEEE 802.11 is different from many of the other IEEE 802 standards because it includes very extensive management capabilities defined at the MAC level. One of the four MAC frame types is dedicated to management frames. There are 11 distinct management frame types. All management frames include: frame control, duration, address 1, 2, and 3, sequence control, framebody and frame check sequence (FCS) fields.

The frame body of a management frame carries information in both fixed fields and in variable length information elements that are dependent on subtype. The information element is a flexible data structure that contains an information element identifier, a length, and the content of the information element. Information elements occur in the frame body in order of increasing identifiers. This arrangement and the data structure itself allow for the flexible extension of the management frames to include new functionality without affecting older implementations. This can be done because older implementations will be able to understand the older elements and will ignore elements with new identifiers. Because the length of the element is part of the data structure, an older implementation can skip over newer elements without needing to understand the content of the element. See Figure 3-11.

The description of the fixed fields and information elements follows the frame descriptions.

Beacon

The Beacon frame is transmitted periodically to allow mobile stations to locate and identify a BSS. The information in a Beacon frame allows a mobile station to locate the BSS (in time and PHY parameters) at any time in the future. The Beacon frame also conveys information to mobile stations about frames that may be buffered during times of low power operation. The Beacon frame includes the following fixed fields: timestamp, beacon interval, and capability information. The timestamp

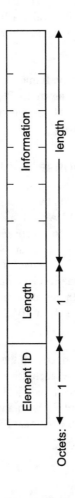

Figure 3-11—Information Element

is a 64-bit field that contains the value of the station's synchronization timer at the time that the frame was transmitted. The beacon interval is the period, measured in "time units" (TU) of 1024 microseconds (μs), of beacon transmissions. The beacon interval is a 16-bit field. The capability information field is a 16-bit field that identifies the capabilities of the station.

The information elements in a Beacon frame are the service set identity (SSID), the supported rates, one or more PHY parameter sets, an optional contention-free parameter set, an optional IBSS parameter set, and an optional traffic indication map.

Probe Request and Response

The probe request frame is transmitted by a mobile station attempting to quickly locate an IEEE 802.11 WLAN. It may be used to locate a WLAN with a particular SSID or to locate any WLAN. The probe request contains two information elements, the SSID and the supported rates. The effect of receiving a probe request is to cause the station to respond with a probe response, if the receiver was the last station in the BSS to transmit a Beacon frame. In an infrastructure BSS, the AP will always respond to the probe requests. In an IBSS, the mobile station that sent the latest Beacon will respond.

The probe response frame contains nearly all the same information as a Beacon frame. The probe response includes the timestamp, beacon interval, and capability information fixed fields. It also includes the SSID, supported rates, one or more PHY parameter sets, the optional contention-free parameter set, and the optional IBSS parameter set.

Authentication

The authentication frame is used to conduct a multiframe exchange between stations that ultimately results in the verification of the identity of each station to the other, within certain constraints. The authentication frame includes three fixed fields: the authentication algorithm number, the authentication transaction sequence number, and the status code. There is also one information element in the authentication frame, the challenge text. The presence of the status code and challenge text in the authentication frame is dependent on the algorithm used and the transaction sequence number.

Deauthentication

The deauthentication frame is used by a station to notify another station of the termination of an authentication relationship. The deauthentication frame includes only a single fixed field, the reason code.

Association Request and Response

The association request and response frames are used by a mobile station to request an association with a BSS and for the success or failure of that request to be returned to the mobile station. The association request frame includes two fixed fields, the capability information field and the listen interval. There are also two information elements in the association request, the SSID and the supported rates.

The association response frame includes three fixed fields: the capability information, the status code, and the association ID. There is one information element in the association response, the supported rates.

Reassociation Request and Response

The reassociation request and response frames are used by a mobile station that has been associated with a BSS and is now associating with another BSS with the same SSID. The reassociation request frame includes the same information as an association request frame, with the addition of a current AP address fixed field.

The reassociation response frame is identical to the association response frame.

Disassociation

The disassociation frame is used by a station to notify another station of the termination of an association relationship. The disassociation frame includes only a single fixed field, the reason code.

Announcement Traffic Indication Message

The announcement traffic indication message (ATIM) frame is used by mobile stations in an IBSS to notify other mobile stations in the IBSS that may have been operating in low power modes that the sender of the ATIM frame has traffic buffered and waiting to be delivered to the station addressed in the ATIM frame. The ATIM frame does not include any fixed fields or information elements.

Components of the Management Frame Body

The components of the management frame body comprise fixed fields and variable length information elements.

Fixed Fields

There are ten fixed fields that may be used in the frame body of management frames. They are: association ID, authentication algorithm number, authentication transaction sequence number, beacon interval, capability information, current AP address, listen interval, reason code, status code, and timestamp.

Association ID

The association ID (AID) is a 16-bit field that contains an arbitrary number assigned by the AP when a station associates with a BSS. The format of this field is identical to that of the duration/ID field of the MAC frame header. The values allowed for this field are 1 through 2007 in the least significant 14 bits. The most significant two bits must both be set to 1. The numeric value in the least significant 14 bits of this field are used by the mobile station to identify which bit in a traffic information map information element indicates that the AP has frames buffered for the mobile station.

Authentication Algorithm Number

The authentication algorithm number is a 16-bit field that contains a number identifying the authentication algorithm to be used to complete an authentication transaction. Currently only two values are defined for this field, all other values are reserved for future standardization. When the authentication algorithm number is 0, the authentication algorithm to be used is "open system." When the authentication algorithm number is 1, the authentication algorithm to be used is "shared key." Each of the algorithms will be described in Chapter 4.

Authentication Transaction Sequence Number

The authentication transaction sequence number is a 16-bit field that is used to track the progress of an authentication transaction. The authentication sequence transaction number is increased sequentially with each authentication frame exchanged during the transaction. The initial value for the authentication transaction sequence number is 1. The authentication transaction sequence number may not take the value 0.

Beacon Interval

The beacon interval field is 16 bits in length. It is a numeric value indicating the typical amount of time that elapses between Beacon frame transmissions. The time interval is measured in time units (TU). One TU is 1024 μs.

Capability Information

The capability information field is 16 bits in length. It is a bit field that indicates the capabilities of a station. The subfields of the capability information field are ESS, IBSS, CF pollable, CF-Poll request, and privacy. In IEEE 802.11b, three additional subfields were added: short preamble, PBCC, and channel agility. See Figure 3-12.

The rules for using the capability information field are complex and dependent on whether the station is an AP or mobile station, or is part of an IBSS. Some subfields are significant only in certain management frames.

The ESS and IBSS subfields are significant only in Beacon and probe response frames. An AP always sets the ESS subfield to 1 and the IBSS subfield to 0. A mobile station in an IBSS always sets the ESS subfield to 0 and the IBSS subfield to 1.

The CF pollable and CF-Poll request subfields are significant in Beacon, probe response, association request, association response, reassociation request, and reassociation response frames. A mobile station will set these subfields in association request and reassociation request frames to indicate its contention-free capability and to request that it be placed on the polling list of the PC. Table 3-3 is taken from IEEE Std 802.11-1997 to describe the functions of these subfields in a mobile station.

An AP will set these subfields in Beacon, probe response, association response, and reassociation response frames to indicate the capability of the PC, if any. Table 3-4 is taken from IEEE Std 802.11-1997 to describe the functions of the subfields in an AP.

In both of these tables, it can be seen that the names of the subfields do not quite match with the functions that are described in the tables. Originally, these two subfields were independent. However, during the

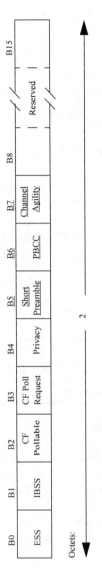

Figure 3-12 — Capability Information Field

Table 3-3—Functions of Subfields in a Mobile Station

CF Pollable	CF-Poll Request	Meaning
0	0	Station is not CF pollable
0	1	Station is CF pollable, not requesting to be placed on the CF-polling list
1	0	Station is CF pollable, requesting to be placed on the CF-polling list
1	1	Station is CF pollable, requesting never to be polled

Table 3-4—Functions of Subfields in an AP

CF Pollable	CF-Poll Request	Meaning
0	0	No PC at AP
0	1	PC at AP for delivery only (no polling)
1	0	PC at AP for delivery and polling
1	1	Reserved

development process of the standard, a case was made for including the ability for a station that does have contention-free polling capabilities to request that it never be polled, but be treated as if it did not have contention-free capability. This left three cases of a station with contention-free capabilities, but only two rows of the table to logically indicate them. At this point the interpretation of the two subfields was changed to be a 2-bit label. It was also decided that the interpretation of the table for the capabilities of the AP be changed similarly.

The privacy subfield is transmitted by the AP in Beacon, probe response, association response, and reassociation response frames. In addition to indicating that the AP implements the Wired Equivalent Privacy algorithm, this subfield also indicates that the use of WEP is required for all data type frames when set to 1. When set to 0, this subfield indicates that the use of WEP is not required.

The short preamble subfield is transmitted by an AP or a mobile station in an IBSS in Beacon, probe response, association response, and reassociation response frames to indicate the availability of the short preamble option when using an IEEE 802.11b PHY. When set to 1, this subfield indicates that the use of short preambles is allowed in the BSS. When set to 0, this subfield indicates that the use of short preamble is not allowed in the BSS.

In a mobile station that is not part of an IBSS, the short preamble subfield in association request and reassociation request frames indicates the capability of the station to send and receive the short preambles of IEEE 802.11b.

The packet binary convolutional coding (PBCC) subfield is transmitted by an AP or a mobile station in an IBSS in Beacon, probe response, association response, and reassociation response frames to indicate the availability of the PBCC option when using an IEEE 802.11b PHY. When set to 1, this subfield indicates that the use of PBCC is allowed in the BSS. When set to 0, this subfield indicates that the use of PBCC is not allowed in the BSS.

In a mobile station that is not part of an IBSS, the PBCC subfield in association request and reassociation request frames indicates the capability of the station to send and receive the PBCC of IEEE 802.11b.

The channel agility subfield indicates that the station is using the channel agility option of IEEE 802.11b.

Current AP Address

The current AP address field is 6 bytes long and is used to hold the address of the AP with which a mobile station is currently associated, when that mobile station is attempting to reassociate. If the reassociation is successful, the AP with which the mobile station has reassociated may use the current AP address to contact that AP and retrieve frames that may have been buffered there for the mobile station.

Listen Interval

The listen interval field is 16 bits long. The listen interval is used by a mobile station to indicate to an AP how long the mobile station may be in low power operating modes and unable to receive frames. The value in the listen interval field is in units of the Beacon interval. For example, a station that wakes only on every tenth Beacon would set this field to 10. The AP may use this field to determine the resources required to support the mobile station and may refuse an association based on that information.

Reason Code

The reason code field is 16 bits long and indicates the reason for an unsolicited notification of disassociation or deauthentication. Table 3-5 is taken from the IEEE 802.11 standard to describe the allowable reasons.

Status Code

The status code field is 16 bits long and indicates the success or failure of a requested operation. The value 0 indicates a successful operation. Any nonzero value indicates the requested operation failed for the indicated reason. Table 3-6 is taken from the IEEE 802.11 standard, with additions made in IEEE 802.11b, to describe the meaning of the status codes.

Timestamp

The timestamp field is a 64-bit number that is the value of the station's TSFTIMER at the time a frame was transmitted. The timestamp field is used in Beacon and probe response frames.

Table 3-5 — Reason Codes

Reason Code	Meaning
0	Reserved
1	Unspecified reason
2	Previous authentication no longer valid
3	Deauthenticated because sending station is leaving (has left) IBSS or ESS
4	Disassociated due to inactivity
5	Disassociated because AP is unable to handle all currently associated stations
6	Class 2 frame received from nonauthenticated station
7	Class 3 frame received from nonassociated station
8	Disassociated because sending station is leaving (has left) BSS
9	Station requesting (re)association is not authenticated with responding station
10–65, 535	Reserved

Table 3-6 — Status Codes

Status Code	Meaning
0	Successful
1	Unspecified failure
2–9	Reserved
10	Cannot support all requested capabilities in the capability information field
11	Reassociation denied due to inability to confirm that association exists
12	Association denied due to reason outside the scope of this standard
13	Responding station does not support the specified authentication algorithm
14	Received an authentication frame with authentication transaction sequence number out of expected sequence
15	Authentication rejected because of challenge failure
16	Authentication rejected due to timeout waiting for next frame in sequence
17	Association denied because AP is unable to handle additional associated stations
18	Association denied due to requesting station not supporting all of the data rates in the BSSBasicRateSet parameter
19	Association denied due to requesting station not supporting the short preamble option.
20	Association denied due to requesting station not supporting the PBCC modulation option.
21	Association denied due to requesting station not supporting the channel agility option.
22–65, 535	Reserved

Information Elements

There are 23 information elements defined by the IEEE 802.11 standard. Table 3-7 is a listing of the individual information elements and their associated element identifier.

Table 3-7 — Information Elements and Associated Element Identifiers

Element ID	Information Element
0	SSID
1	Supported rates
2	FH parameter set
3	DS parameter set
4	CF parameter set
5	TIM
6	IBSS parameter set
7–15	Reserved
16	Challenge text
17–31	Reserved for challenge text extension
32–255	Reserved

Service Set Identity

The service set identity (SSID) information element is identified by element ID 0. This information element carries the SSID of the

IEEE 802.11 WLAN. The length of the SSID may be up to 32 bytes. There is no restriction on the format or content of the SSID. It may be a null-terminated string of ASCII characters or a multibyte binary value. The choice of the value and format of the SSID is entirely up to the network administrator or user. There is one special case for the SSID, when the length of it is zero. In this case, the SSID is considered to be the "broadcast" identity. The broadcast identity is used in probe request frames when the mobile station is attempting to discover all IEEE 802.11 WLANs in its vicinity.

Supported Rates

The supported rates element describes the data rates that the station supports. The element may contain from 1 to 8 bytes of rate information. Each byte represents a single rate, with the lower 7 bits of the byte representing the rate value, and the most significant bit indicating whether the rate is mandatory or not. In the original standard, the values describing the rates in this element were mathematically related to the actual data rate. The rates were measured in units of 500 kbit/s. In IEEE 802.11b, the interpretation of the values for the supported rates was changed. The values now are simple labels that are associated with particular data rates. This change was made because of the upper limit of 63.5 Mbit/s the original interpretation imposed on the data rates. With the new interpretation from IEEE 802.11b, there is no upper limit on the data rate imposed by the supported rates element.

The supported rates element is transmitted in Beacon, probe response, association request, association response, reassociation request, and reassociation response frames. In frames other than the association request and reassociation request, the rates indicated as mandatory must be supported by a station that desires to be associated with a particular BSS. If a station does not support all of the rates indicated to be mandatory, it may not associate with the BSS. If it attempts to associate with the BSS, the response from the AP will indicate a failure to associate, with a status code of 18.

FH Parameter Set

The FH parameter set element, as well as the DS parameter set, CF parameter set, and IBSS parameter set elements, are different from the other information elements in that they are not variable in length. They are information elements rather than fixed fields because their presence in management frames is dependent on whether particular options are implemented. In this case, the FH parameter set element is present in Beacon and probe response frames only if the PHY being used is the IEEE 802.11 FHSS PHY or the IEEE 802.11b PHY with the channel agility option enabled. Otherwise, this element is not present. It is because of the conditional nature of this element, and the others mentioned, that it is an element rather than a fixed field. Making it an information element allows the fixed fields of the management frames to be invariant with respect to the PHY or options in use.

The FH parameter set element is 7 bytes long. In addition to the two bytes for the element ID and length, the element contains the dwell time, hop set, hop pattern, and hop index. The description of these items can be found in Chapter 6.

DS Parameter Set

The DS parameter set element is 3 bytes long. In addition to the element ID and length, it contains the current channel. This element is present in Beacon and probe response frames only if the IEEE 802.11 DSSS or IEEE 802.11b PHY is being used. The description of these items can be found in Chapter 6.

CF Parameter Set

The CF parameter set element is 8 bytes long. In addition to the element ID and length, this element contains the CFP count, CFP period, CFP max duration, and CFP duration remaining. This element is present in Beacon and probe response frames only if a PC is in operation in the BSS.

Traffic Indication Map

The traffic indication map (TIM) element may be from 6 to 256 bytes long. This element carries information about frames that are buffered at the AP for stations in power saving modes of operation. For a description of how the TIM is used, see Chapter 4. In addition to the element ID and the length fields, the TIM element contains four more fields, the DTIM count, DTIM period, bitmap control, and the partial virtual bitmap.

The delivery TIM (DTIM) count and DTIM period are used to inform mobile stations when multicast frames that have been buffered at the AP will be delivered and how often that delivery will occur. The AP will buffer all multicast traffic when there are any mobile stations operating in low power modes. (See Chapter 4 for further information.) The DTIM count is an integer value that counts down to zero. This value represents the number of Beacon frames that will occur before the delivery of multicast frames. When the DTIM count is zero, multicast traffic will be sent. The DTIM period is the number of Beacon frames between multicast frame deliveries. The DTIM period has a significant effect on the maximum power savings a station may achieve, if the station is to receive multicast traffic. The larger the DTIM period, the greater the power savings that may be achieved, since a station may spend a larger proportion of its time in a low power state. Of course, the DTIM period must be balanced with the overall performance of protocols that depend on multicast traffic, as a larger DTIM period will increase the delay before multicast frames are delivered to all stations.

The bitmap control and partial virtual bitmap are used to provide information to stations that have been operating in low power modes about frames that are buffered at the AP. When each station associates, it is assigned an AID. The value of the AID designates the individual bit in the partial virtual bitmap that, when set, indicates that there is at least one frame buffered at the AP for that station.

The entire bitmap is 2008 bits long and is not transmitted with each Beacon frame. Only that portion of the bitmap that is necessary to inform stations of buffered frames is sent. This is accomplished by using the bitmap control field to identify the starting point of the partial bitmap that is transmitted. The starting point of the partial bitmap is the first byte of the complete bitmap that is nonzero. The ending point of the partial bitmap is the last byte of the complete bitmap that is nonzero.

Seven bits are used in the bitmap control field to represent the starting point of the partial virtual bitmap. The value of these seven bits is N1/2, where N1 is the largest even number such that bits numbered 1 through (N1 × 8) − 1 in the bitmap are all 0. The endpoint of the partial virtual bitmap is represented by N2, where N2 is the smallest number such that bits numbered (N2 + 1) × 8 through 2007 in the bitmap are all 0. The value of the length field of the TIM element is set to (N2 − N1) + 4.

There is one special case, AID 0. AID 0 is defined to represent buffered multicast frames and is never assigned to an associating station. The bit representing AID 0 is not used in the virtual bitmap and is always zero. The bit representing AID 0 is carried in the bitmap control field.

IBSS Parameter Set

The IBSS parameter set element is another fixed length information element, defined as an information element rather than a fixed field because it will occur in Beacon frames only in an IBSS. In addition to the element ID and length, there is one more field in this information element, the ATIM window field. The announcement TIM (ATIM) window field is 16-bits long and indicates the length of the ATIM window after each Beacon frame transmission in an IBSS. The length of the ATIM window is indicated in TU.

Challenge Text

The challenge text information element may be up to 255 bytes long. In addition to the element ID and length fields, this element carries one more field, the challenge text. The challenge text field may be up to 253 bytes long. There are no format or content restrictions on the challenge text field.

Other MAC Operations

Fragmentation

The wireless medium on which the IEEE 802.11 WLAN operates is unlike wired media in many ways. One of the most significant ways that it differs from wired media is the presence of uncontrollable interference, particularly in the 2.4 GHz radio band, that can render communication between WLAN stations nearly impossible. In addition to other communication users of the 2.4 GHz band, this band is also a worldwide industrial, scientific, and medical (ISM) band. Probably the most widespread equipment using this band is the conventional microwave oven.

A microwave oven produces its microwave radiation using a magnetron. To keep the cost of the oven to a minimum, the magnetron is typically powered by a half-wave rectified power supply. This causes the magnetron to be emitting radiation through half of each 60 Hz power cycle (in the US). In other words, the magnetron is radiating for 8 ms of every 16 ms. In addition, the frequency of operation of the magnetron changes as the power supply ramps up and down, sweeping the radiation across a large portion of the band.

To operate in the presence of this known interferer, the IEEE 802.11 MAC can fragment its frames in an attempt to increase the probability that they will be delivered without errors induced by the interference. Frames longer than the fragmentation threshold are fragmented prior to the initial transmission into fragments no longer than the value of the dot11FragmentationThreshold MIB attribute. A frame will be divided into one or more fragments equal in length to the fragmentation threshold and no more that one fragment smaller than the fragmentation threshold. The default value of the fragmentation threshold is such that no frames will be fragmented. The value may be changed to begin fragmenting frames. If the interference source is known, such as the microwave oven, the value of the fragmentation threshold may be calculated from the characteristics of the interferer and the bit rate of the transmissions.

When a frame is fragmented, the sequence control field of the frame header indicates the placement of the individual fragment among the set of fragments. The more fragments bit in the frame control field indicates whether the current fragment is the last fragment. The fragments are transmitted in order by their fragment numbers in the sequence control field. The lowest numbered fragment is transmitted first. Subsequent fragments are transmitted immediately upon receiving the acknowledgment of the previous fragment, without needing to compete for the medium again. This is called a fragment burst. IEEE 802.11 uses fragment bursts to minimize the total amount of time that is taken to deliver a single frame that has been fragmented, when all of the fragments are delivered on the first attempt. If a fragment is not delivered on the first attempt, subsequent fragments are not transmitted until the previous fragment has been acknowledged. If a fragment is not acknowledged, the normal rules for retransmission of frames apply. See Figure 3-13.

The duration calculation during a fragment burst is slightly different from that of the calculation during a single frame transmission. For a fragment burst, the calculation of duration for the RTS and CTS frames, if any, is unchanged. The duration calculated for the data and ACK frames changes, however. Normally, the duration value in a Data frame is calculated from the end of the data frame to the end of the ACK frame that is expected to follow. In a fragment burst, the duration value in a data frame is similar to that of the RTS frame and is calculated from the end of the current fragment to the end of the subsequent fragment, including the ACK frame that is interposed. Similarly, the duration calculated for an ACK frame in a fragment burst is like that of the CTS frame. It is calculated from the end of the current ACK frame to the end of the subsequent ACK frame and includes the data frame that is interposed. This modified calculation of the duration for data and ACK frames is used throughout the fragment burst, except for the last Data frame, the one that has the more fragments bit clear, and the final ACK frame. For these two final frames of a fragment burst, the duration calculation reverts to the normal duration calculation. The duration of the final data frame will be calculated from the end of the data frame to the end of the ACK frame. The value of the duration in the final ACK frame is zero. See Figure 3-14.

Privacy

IEEE 802.11 incorporates MAC-level privacy mechanisms to protect the content of data frames from eavesdropping. This is, again, because the medium for the IEEE 802.11 WLAN is significantly different from that of a wired LAN. The WLAN lacks even the minimal privacy provided by a wired LAN. The wired LAN must be physically compromised in order to tap its data. A WLAN, by contrast, can be compromised by anyone with a suitable antenna. The IEEE 802.11 Wired Equivalent Privacy (WEP) mechanism provides protection at a level that is felt to be equivalent to that of a wired LAN.

WEP is an encryption mechanism that takes the content of a data frame, its frame body, and passes it through an encryption algorithm. The result then replaces the frame body of the data frame and is transmitted. Data frames that are encrypted are sent with the WEP bit in the frame control field of the MAC header set. The receiver of an encrypted data frame passes the encrypted frame body through the same encryption algorithm used by the sending station. The result is the original, unencrypted frame body. The receiver then passes the unencrypted result up to higher layer protocols.

It should be noted that only the frame body of data frames is encrypted. This leaves the complete MAC header of the data frame, and the entire frame of other frame types, unencrypted and available to even the casual eavesdropper. Thus, WEP does provide protection for the content of the data frames, but does not protect against other security threats to a LAN, such as traffic analysis.

The encryption algorithm used in IEEE 802.11 is RC4. RC4 was developed by Ron Rivest of RSA Data Security, Inc. (RSADSI). RSADSI is

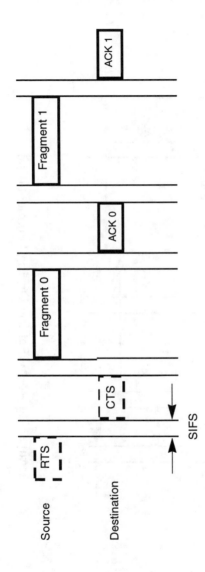

Figure 3-13 — Fragmentation of a Data Frame

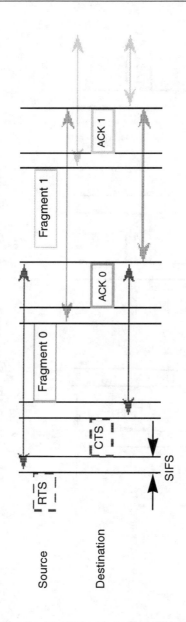

Figure 3-14 — NAV Setting During Fragmentation

now part of Network Associates, Inc. RC4 is a symmetric stream cipher that supports a variable length key. A symmetric cipher is one that uses the same key and algorithm for both encryption and decryption. A stream cipher is an algorithm that can process an arbitrary number of bytes. This is contrasted with a block cipher that processes a fixed number of bytes. The key is the one piece of information that must be shared by both the encrypting and decrypting stations. It is the key that allows every station to use the same algorithm, but only those stations sharing the same key can correctly decrypt encrypted frames. RC4 allows the key length to be variable, up to 256 bytes, as opposed to requiring the key to be fixed at a certain length. IEEE 802.11 has chosen to use a 40-bit key.

The IEEE 802.11 standard describes the use of the RC4 algorithm and the key in WEP. However, key distribution or key negotiation is not mentioned in the standard. This leaves much of the most difficult part of secure communications to the individual manufacturers of IEEE 802.11 equipment. In a secure communication system using a symmetric algorithm, such as RC4, it is imperative that the keys used by the algorithm be protected, that they remain secret. If a key is compromised, all frames encrypted with that key are also compromised. Thus, while it is likely that equipment from many manufacturers will be able to interoperate and exchange encrypted frames, it is unlikely that a single mechanism will be available that will securely place the keys in the individual stations. There is currently discussion in the IEEE 802.11 working group to address this lack of standardization.

WEP Details

IEEE 802.11 provides two mechanisms to select a key for use when encrypting or decrypting a frame. The first mechanism is a set of as many as four default keys. Default keys are intended to be shared by all stations in a BSS or an ESS. The benefit of using a default key is that, once the station obtains the default keys, a station can communicate securely with all of the other stations in a BSS or ESS. The problem with using default keys is that they are widely distributed to many stations and may be more likely to be revealed. The second mechanism provided by IEEE 802.11 allows a station to establish a "key mapping" relationship with another station. Key mapping allows a station to create a key that is used with only one other station. Though this one to one mapping is not a requirement of the standard, this would be the most secure way for a station to operate, since there would be only one other station that would have knowledge of each key used. The fewer stations possessing a key, the less likely the key will be revealed.

The dot11PrivacyInvoked attribute controls the use of WEP in a station. If dot11PirvacyInvoked is false, all frames are sent without encryption. If dot11PrivacyInvoked is true, all frames will be sent with encryption, unless encryption is disabled for specific destinations. Encryption for specific destinations may only be disabled if a key mapping relationship exists with that destination.

A default key may be used to encrypt a frame only when a key mapping relationship does not exist between the sending and receiving station. When a frame is to be sent using a default key, the station determines if any default keys are available. There are four possible default keys that might be available. A key is available if its entry in the dot11WEPDefaultKeysTable is not null. If one or more default keys is available, the station chooses one key, by an algorithm not defined in the standard, and uses it to encrypt the frame body of the frame to be sent. The WEP header and trailer are appended to the encrypted frame body, the default key used to encrypt the frame is indicated in the KeyID of the header portion along with the initialization vector, and the integrity check value (ICV) in the trailer. If there are no available default keys, i.e., all default keys are null, the frame is discarded. See Figure 3-15.

If a key mapping relationship exists between the source and destination stations, the "key mapping key," the key shared only by the source and destination stations, must be used to encrypt frames sent to that destination. When a frame is to be sent using a key mapping key, the key corresponding to the destination of the frame is chosen from the

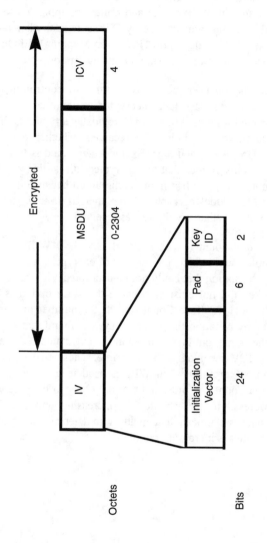

Figure 3-15 — WEP Expansion of the Frame Body

dot11WEPKeyMappingsTable, if the dot11WEPKeyMappingWEPOn entry for the destination is true. The frame body is encrypted using the key mapping key, and the WEP header and trailer are appended to the encrypted frame body. The value of the KeyID is set to zero when a key mapping key is used. If the value of dot11WEPKeyMappingWEPOn for the destination is false, the frame is sent without encryption.

Corresponding to the dot11PrivacyInvoked attribute controlling the sending of frames, the dot11ExcludeUnencrypted attribute controls the reception of encrypted frames. When dot11ExcludeUnencrypted is false, all frames addressed to the station are received, whether they are encrypted or not. However when dot11ExcludeUnencrypted is true, the station will receive only frames that are encrypted, discarding all data frames that are not encrypted. If a frame is discarded because it is not encrypted and dot11ExcludeUnencrypted is true, there is no indication to the higher layer protocols that any frame was received.

There are two counters associated with WEP. The dot11UndecryptableCount reflects the number of encrypted frames that were received by the station that could not be decrypted, either because a corresponding key did not exist or because the WEP option is not implemented. The dot11ICVErrorCount reflects the number of frames that were received by a station for which a key was found that should have decrypted the frame, but that resulted in the calculated ICV value not matching the ICV received with the frame. These two counters should be monitored carefully when WEP is used in a WLAN. The dot11UndecryptableCount can indicated that an attack to deny service may be in progress, if the counter is increasing rapidly. The dot11ICVErrorCount can indicate that an attack to determine a key is in progress, if this counter is increasing rapidly.

Chapter 4
MAC Management

IEEE 802.11 is the first LAN standard by the IEEE 802 committee that includes significant management capabilities. This is because an IEEE 802.11 WLAN must deal with an environment that is measurably more complex than those of the wired LAN standards of IEEE 802. The largest challenge for the IEEE 802.11 WLAN is that the medium is not a wire. It is this simple fact that leads to all of the other obstacles that IEEE 802.11 must overcome in order to offer the same reliable service expected of an IEEE 802 LAN.

Because the media over which the IEEE 802.11 WLAN operate are not wires, the media are shared by other users that have no concept of data communication or sharing the media. An example of this type of user is the common microwave oven. The microwave oven operates in the 2.4 GHz ISM band because one excitation frequency of the water molecule lies in this band. The oven operates by transferring energy to the water molecules in food, thereby heating the food. Another user in this same band is the radio frequency ID (RFID) tag. RFID tags are usually small, cheap, unpowered devices that receive their power from a microwave beam and then return a unique identifier. RFID tags are used to track retail inventory, identify rail cars, and many other uses. An unfortunate consequence of these devices sharing the band with WLANs is that some of this microwave energy leaks from the oven and is purposely broadcast for RFID tags, thus, interfering with the operation of the WLAN.

There are also other WLANs than IEEE 802.11 that share the media. This would be somewhat equivalent to attempting to run IEEE 802.3, IEEE 802.5, IEEE 802.12, and fiber distributed data interference (FDDI) on the same twisted pair cable, simultaneously. These other WLAN users of the media are often uncoordinated with IEEE 802.11 and, in most cases, do not provide for any mechanism to share the media at all. Finally, there are other IEEE 802.11 WLANs sharing the media.

These other users of the media result in the first challenge for the IEEE 802.11 WLAN, an intermittent connection to the media and other stations of the IEEE 802.11 WLAN. Much of the management specified in IEEE 802.11 is to deal with the intermittent nature of the media.

The second challenge to be dealt with by an IEEE 802.11 WLAN is that anyone can "connect" to the WLAN, simply by erecting the right kind of antenna. This leads to the need to identify the stations connecting to the WLAN, in order to allow only the stations authorized to do so to use the WLAN, and also to the need to protect the information sent over the WLAN from improper interception by eavesdroppers.

The third challenge to be dealt with by an IEEE 802.11 WLAN is mobility. Once the wires are removed from a LAN, the natural thing to do is to pick up the equipment connected to the LAN and move it around, taking it from an office to a conference room or to another building. Thus, IEEE 802.11 equipment is not always in the same place from one moment to the next. Even if the equipment were to remain in a fixed location, the nature of the wireless media may make it appear as if the equipment has moved. Dealing with mobility while making all of the expected LAN services available is a problem to be solved by MAC management.

The final challenge to be dealt with by an IEEE 802.11 WLAN is power management. Another consequence of doing away with wired media and enabling the equipment to be mobile is that much of the equipment will be run on batteries. Conserving the energy stored in the batteries to allow the equipment to operate for as long as possible must be built into the WLAN protocol and controlled by MAC management.

Tools Available to Meet the Challenges

The IEEE 802.11 standard defines a number of MAC management capabilities that are designed to meet the challenges of operating a reliable WLAN. These tools are: authentication, association, address filtering, privacy, power management, and synchronization.

Authentication

Authentication provides a mechanism for one station to prove its identity to another station in the WLAN. The process of authentication is the exchange of questions, assertions, and results. An example of this would be station A asserting "I am station A," and asking station B "Who are you?" At this point the process of authentication varies dependent on the particular algorithm in use. It may proceed with station B saying "OK, prove you are station A" and asserting "I am station B." Station A would then offer some proof of its identity and request that same kind of proof from station B. If the proofs exchanged were acceptable, each station would then tell the other that its assertion of identity is believed.

Authentication can be used between any two stations. However, it is most useful when used between a mobile station and an AP in an infrastructure LAN. In this case, the AP is the point of entry for any mobile station into the ESS and, possibly, into the wired LAN behind the ESS. Full proof of the identity of a mobile station is necessary if the network is to be protected from unauthorized users.

As it is defined in IEEE 802.11, there are two authentication algorithms available. The first algorithm, open system authentication, is not really an authentication algorithm at all. It is a placeholder for those users of IEEE 802.11 that do not wish to implement the WEP algorithms necessary for stronger authentication. Open system authentication allows the authentication frame exchange protocol to complete with a guaranteed result of "success." In this case, station A would assert its identity to station B, and station B would respond with a successful result for the authentication. There is no verification of the identity of either station. If any control over the stations allowed to participate in the IEEE 802.11 WLAN is desired, this authentication algorithm should not be used.

The second authentication algorithm is the shared key authentication algorithm. This algorithm depends on both stations having a copy of a shared WEP key. This algorithm uses the WEP encryption option to encrypt and decrypt a "challenge text" as the proof that the stations share the same key. Beginning the authentication process, station A sends its identity assertion to station B. Station B responds to the assertion with an assertion of its own and a request to station A to prove its identity by correctly encrypting the challenge text. Station A encrypts the challenge text (actually the entire frame body of the authentication management frame) using the normal WEP encryption rules, including use of default and key mapping keys, and sends the result back to station B. Station B decrypts the frame using the appropriate key and returns an authentication management frame to station A with the success or failure of the authentication indicated. If the authentication is successful, the standard says that each station is authenticated to the other.

A station may authenticate with any number of other stations. The standard does not place a limit on the number of authentications that may be processed. This allows a station to pre-authenticate with other stations, even though there may be no immediate need for this. In later examples, the desirability of pre-authentication will be shown.

It should be noted that this algorithm really only authenticates station A to station B. The IEEE 802.11 Working Group believed that the AP somehow occupied a more privileged position than the mobile stations when it came to authentication, since it is always the mobile station that initiates the authentication process. It is for this reason that it is only the mobile station that performs the encryption operation on the challenge text. This leaves the IEEE 802.11 WLAN open to some not so subtle security problems. In particular, a rogue AP could adopt the SSID of the ESS and announce its presence through the normal beaconing process. This would cause mobile stations to attempt to authenticate with the rogue. The rogue could always complete the authentication process with an indication of successful authentication. This would cause mobile stations to attempt to use the rogue for access to the WLAN. The rogue could then simply complete normal frame handshake procedures and the mobile stations would be the victims of a denial of service attack. A more active rogue could use more subtle means to attempt to gain access to the content of higher layer protocol frames containing user names, passwords, and other sensitive data. However, if the data is encrypted using WEP, it is highly unlikely that the rogue could successfully decrypt the information.

Fortunately for those interested in greater security for their WLANs, the IEEE 802.11 Working Group is currently discussing extensions to the authentication algorithms that will provide cryptographically secure, bidirectional authentication.

Association

Association is the mechanism through which IEEE 802.11 provides transparent mobility to stations. Because IEEE 802.11 is designed to operate without wires tethering a piece of LAN equipment to a single location, support for mobility is built into the standard. Association is the process of a mobile station "connecting" to an AP and requesting service from the WLAN. Association may only be accomplished after a successful authentication has been completed.

When a mobile station requests to be connected to the WLAN, it sends an association request to an AP. The association request includes information on the capabilities of the station, such as the data rates it supports, the high rate PHY options it supports, its contention-free capabilities, its support of WEP, and any request for contention-free services. The association request also includes information about the length of time that the station may be in a low power operating mode.

The information in an association request is used by the AP to decide whether to grant the association for the mobile station. The policies and algorithms used by the AP to make this decision are not described in the standard. Some things that may be considered are supporting all of the required data rates and PHY options, requiring contention-free services beyond the ability of the AP to support, long periods in low power operation that require excessive buffer commitments from the AP, and the number of stations currently associated. Because the standard does not specify what information may be considered by the AP when deciding to grant an association, information not local to the AP may also be used, such as load balancing factors and availability of other APs nearby. When the AP responds to the mobile station with an association response, the response includes a status indication. The status indication provides the mobile station with the success or failure of the association request. If the request fails, the reason for that failure is in the status indication.

Once a station is associated, the AP is responsible for forwarding data frames from the mobile station toward their destination. The destination of the data frames may be in the same BSS as the mobile station, in which case the AP will simply transmit the data frame to the BSS, or it may be outside of the BSS. If the destination of a data frame is outside the BSS, the AP will send the frame into the DS. The use of the DS is outside of the scope of the IEEE 802.11 standard. However, most vendors of IEEE 802.11 equipment either bridge or route data frames from the BSS to the wired network serving as the DS. If the destination of the data frame is another mobile station in a different BSS, the AP sends the frame to the AP of the other BSS, where it will be forwarded to the mobile station. If the destination of the frame is entirely outside the ESS, the AP will forward the frame to the "portal," the exit from the DS to the rest of the network. A portal is simply a transfer point between the wired LAN and the ESS, where frames *logically* enter the ESS. A portal may be an AP, a bridge, or a router. Because IEEE 802.11 is one of the family of IEEE 802 standards, an IEEE 802.11 frame must be translated from the IEEE 802.11 format to the format of the other LAN. This translation should be done according to IEEE Std 802.1h for bridging IEEE 802.11 to another LAN. The entire IEEE 802.11 frame, including MAC header and FCS, should not be encapsulated within another MAC protocol.

Similarly, when a data frame is sent from outside the ESS to a mobile station, the portal must forward the frame to the correct AP, the one that has the mobile station associated in its BSS. The need for the portal to know where the mobile stations are implies that there must be information kept in the DS allowing each mobile station that is associated to be found at any given instant in time. Again, this is not specified in the

IEEE 802.11 standard, but is a required function of the DS to support the operation of the mobile stations as the move from one AP to another.

Once a station is successfully associated, it may begin exchanging data frames with the AP. Because the station is mobile and also because the medium is subject to both slow and fast variations, the mobile station will eventually lose contact with the AP. When this occurs, the mobile station must begin a new association in order to continue exchanging data frames. Because the DS must maintain information about the location of each mobile station and because data frames may have been sent to an AP with which the mobile station no longer can communicate, a mobile station will use a reassociation request after its initial association. The reassociation request includes all of the information in the original association request, plus the address of the last AP with which the station was associated. The last AP's address allows the AP receiving the reassociation request to retrieve any frames at the old AP and deliver them to the mobile station. Once the AP grants the reassociation, the mobile station's older association is terminated. While this is outside the scope of the current standard, the AP that has just granted the reassociation normally communicates with the AP with which the station was last associated to cause the termination of the old association. The reason for this should be clear. The association provides information to the DS about the location of the mobile station. The mobile station is allowed to have only one location in the ESS so that there is no ambiguity as to where frames destined for that mobile station should be sent. Thus, the station is permitted only a single association.

Address Filtering (MAC Function)

The address filtering mechanism in the IEEE 802.11 WLAN is a bit more complex than that of other IEEE 802 LANs. In a WLAN it is not sufficient to make receive decisions on the destination address alone. There may be more than one IEEE 802.11 WLAN operating in the same location and on the same medium and channel. In this case, the receiver must examine more than the destination address to make correct receive decisions. IEEE 802.11 incorporates at least three addresses in every data and management frame that may be received by a station. In addition to the destination address, these frames also include the BSS identifier. A station must use both the destination address and the BSSID when making receive decisions, according to the standard. This ensures that the station will discard frames sent from a BSS other than that with which it is associated. Filtering on the BSSID is particularly important to minimize the number of multicast frames with which the station must deal.

Privacy (MAC Function)

The privacy function is provided by the WEP mechanism described in Chapter 3. WEP allows the frames to be broadcast and received by any receiver, because the content of the frames may be protected by a well known encryption algorithm. Further details of the operation of WEP are provided in Chapter 3.

Power Management

The power management mechanism is the most complex part of the IEEE 802.11 standard. It allows mobile stations, in either an independent BSS or an infrastructure BSS, to enter low power modes of operation where they turn off their receiver and transmitter to conserve power. Because of the significant differences between the independent and infrastructure BSSs, there are two different mechanisms for power management. One of the mechanisms is used only in independent BSSs and the other only in infrastructure BSSs.

Power Management in an Independent BSS

In an independent BSS (IBSS), power management is a fully distributed process, managed by the individual mobile stations. Power management comprises two parts: the functions of the station entering a low power operating mode and the functions of the stations that desire to communicate with that station. For a station to enter a low power operating state, a state where it has turned off the receiver and transmitter to conserve power, the station must successfully complete a data frame handshake with another station with the power management bit set in the frame header. Any other station is acceptable for this handshake. No requirement exists for the station to complete this handshake with more than a single other station, even though there may be many other stations with which this station has communicated in the BSS. If the station has no data to send, it may use the null function subtype of the data frame for this handshake. Until this frame handshake is completed, the station must remain in the awake state. The IEEE 802.11 standard does not specify when a station may enter or leave a low power operating state, only how the transition is to take place.

Once the station has successfully completed the frame handshake with the power management bit set, it may enter the power saving state. In the power saving state, the station must wake up to receive every Beacon transmission. The station must also stay awake for a period of time after each Beacon, called the announcement or ad hoc traffic indication message window (ATIM). The earliest the station may reenter the power saving state is at the conclusion of the ATIM window. The reason that a station must remain awake during the ATIM window is that other stations that are attempting to send frames to it will announce those frames during the ATIM window. If the power saving station receives an ATIM frame, it must acknowledge that frame and remain awake until the end of the next ATIM window, following the next Beacon frame, in order to allow the other station to send its data frame.

For a station desiring to send a frame to another station in an IBSS, the standard requires that the sending station estimate the power saving state of the intended destination. The estimate of the power saving state of another station may be based on the last data frame received from the station and on other information local to the sending station. How the sending station creates its estimate of the power saving state of the intended destination is not described in the standard. If the sending station determines that the intended destination is in the power saving state, the sending station may not transmit its frame until after it has received an acknowledgment of an ATIM frame, sent during the ATIM window, from the intended destination. Once an acknowledgment of the ATIM is received, the station will send the corresponding data frame after the conclusion of the ATIM window.

Multicast frames must also be announced by the sending station during the ATIM window before they may be transmitted. The ATIM is sent to the same multicast address as the data frame that will be sent subsequently. Because the ATIM is sent to a multicast address, no acknowledgment will be generated, nor is one expected. Any stations that wish to receive the announced multicast data frame must stay awake until the end of the next ATIM window, after the next Beacon frame. The station sending the multicast data frame may send it at any time after the conclusion of the ATIM window.

This power management mechanism puts a slightly greater burden on the sending station than on the receiving station. Sending stations must send an announcement frame in addition to the data frame it desires to deliver to the destination. Sending stations must buffer the frames to be sent to the power saving destination until the destination awakens and acknowledges the ATIM. Because of the nature of the wireless medium, it may require several attempts before an ATIM is acknowledged. Each transmission of an ATIM consumes power at the sending station. The receiving station must awaken for every Beacon and ATIM window, but need not make any transmissions unless it receives an ATIM frame. This power management mechanism allows reasonable power savings in all mobile stations. However, there is a minimum duty cycle required of both senders and destinations, in the ratio of the time of the ATIM window to the time of the beacon period, that limits the maximum power savings that may be achieved. During the development of the IEEE 802.11 standard, the limitation of the maximum power savings was thought to be a reasonable trade-off for the complexity involved.

Power Management in an Infrastructure BSS

In an infrastructure BSS, the power management mechanism is central-ized in the AP. This power management mechanism allows much greater power savings for mobile stations than does the mechanism used in IBSSs. This is so because the AP assumes all of the burden of buffer-ing data frames for power saving stations and delivering them when the stations request, allowing the mobile stations to remain in their power saving state for much longer periods.

The responsibilities of the mobile stations in an infrastructure BSS are to inform the AP, in its association request, of the number of beacon periods that the station will be in its power saving mode, to awaken at the expected time of a Beacon transmission to learn if there are any data frames waiting, and to complete a successful frame handshake with the AP, while the power management bit is set, to inform the AP when the station will enter the power saving mode. A mobile station can achieve much deeper power savings than in the IBSS, because it is not required to awaken for every Beacon, nor to stay awake for any length of time after the Beacons for which it does awaken. The mobile station must also awaken at times determined by the AP, when multicast frames are to be delivered. This time is indicated in the Beacon frames as the deliv-ery traffic indication map (DTIM). If the mobile station is to receive multicast frames, it must be awake at every DTIM.

The AP will buffer data frames for each power saving station that it has associated. It will also buffer all multicast frames if it has any stations associated that are in the power saving mode. The data frames will remain buffered at the AP for a minimum time not less than the number of Beacon periods indicated in the mobile station's association request. The IEEE 802.11 standard indicates that an AP may use an aging algo-rithm to discard buffered frames that are older than it is required to pre-serve, though a specific algorithm is not described. Once the AP has frames buffered for a power saving station, it will indicate this in the traffic indication map (TIM) sent with each Beacon frame. Every station that is associated with the AP is assigned an AID during the association process. The AID indicates a single bit in the TIM that reflects the status of frames buffered for that station. When the bit in the TIM is set, there is at least one frame buffered for the corresponding station. When the bit is clear, there are no frames buffered for the corresponding station. A special AID, AID zero, is dedicated to indicating the status of buffered multicast traffic. The AP will send the TIM, updated with the latest buffer status, with every Beacon.

If an AP has any buffered multicast frames, those frames are sent immediately after the Beacon announcing the DTIM. If there is more than one multicast frame to be sent, the AP will indicate this fact by setting the more data bit in the frame control field of each multicast frame except for the last to be sent. Following the transmission of any buffered multicast frames, the AP will send frames to active stations and to those stations that have requested the delivery of frames buffered for them. A mobile station requests delivery of buffered frames by sending a PS-Poll frame to the AP. The AP will respond to each PS-Poll by sending one frame to the requesting station. In the frame control field of the frame sent in response to the PS-Poll, the AP will set the more data bit if there are further frames buffered for the station. The station is required to send a PS-Poll to the AP for each data frame it receives with the more data bit set. This ensures that the station will empty the buffer of the frames held for it by the AP. The standard does not state any time requirement for the station to send the PS-Poll after seeing the more data bit. Thus, some implementations may rapidly retrieve all buffered frames from the AP and others may operate at a much more leisurely pace.

An AP that is also a PC running a contention-free period (CFP) will use the CFP to deliver buffered frames to stations that are CF Pollable. It may also use the CFP to deliver multicast frames after the DTIM is announced.

Synchronization

Synchronization is the process of the stations in a BSS getting in step with each other, so that reliable communication is possible. The MAC provides the synchronization mechanism to allow support of physical (PHY) layers that make use of frequency hopping or other time-based mechanisms where the parameters of the PHY layer change with time. The process involves beaconing, to announce the presence of a BSS, and scanning, to find a BSS. Once a BSS is found, a station joins the BSS. This process is entirely distributed, in both independent and infrastructure BSSs, and relies on a common timebase, provided by a timer synchronization function (TSF).

The TSF maintains a 64-bit timer running at 1 MHz and updated by information from other stations. The tolerance of the time is 25 ppm. When a station begins operation, it resets the timer to zero. The timer may be updated by information received in Beacon frames, as described below.

Timer Synchronization in an Infrastructure BSS

In an infrastructure BSS, the AP is responsible for transmitting a Beacon frame periodically. The time between Beacon frames is called the beacon period and is included as part of the information in the Beacon frame, in order to inform stations receiving the Beacon when to expect the next Beacon. The AP will attempt to transmit the Beacon frame at the target Beacon transmission time (TBTT), when the value of the TSF timer of the AP, modulo the beacon period, is zero. The Beacon, however, is a frame like any other and is sent using the same rules for accessing the medium. Thus, the Beacon may be delayed beyond the TBTT due to other traffic occupying the medium and backoff delays. In addition, because the Beacon is sent to the broadcast address, it will not be retransmitted should the frame be corrupted. This may result in the Beacon not being received by some, or all, of the stations in the BSS. This is an expected consequence of the normal operation of the IEEE 802.11 WLAN and does not result in any degradation of the operation of the LAN. Without regard to whether the Beacon frame was sent at the TBTT or if it was corrupted, the AP will attempt to transmit the following Beacon at the next TBTT. In a lightly loaded BSS, the Beacon will usually be sent at the TBTT and be spaced apart by exactly the beacon period. As the load in the BSS increases, the Beacon will be delayed beyond the TBTT more often.

The TSF timer in an AP is reset to zero upon initialization of the AP and is then incremented by the 1 MHz clock of the AP. At the time of each Beacon, the current value of the timer is inserted in the Beacon frame. For a mobile station in an infrastructure BSS, the synchronization function is very simple. A mobile station will update its TSF timer with the value of the timer it receives from the AP in the Beacon frame, modified by any processing time required to perform the update operation. Thus, the timer values in all of the mobile stations in the BSS receiving the Beacon are synchronized to that of the AP.

Timer Synchronization in an IBSS

In an IBSS, there is no AP to act as the central time source for the BSS. In an IBSS, the timer synchronization mechanism is completely distributed among the mobile stations of the BSS. Since there is no AP, the mobile station that starts the BSS will begin by resetting its TSF timer to zero and transmitting a Beacon, choosing a beacon period. This establishes the basic beaconing process for this BSS. After the BSS has been established, each station in the IBSS will attempt to send a Beacon after the TBTT arrives. To be sure that at least one Beacon frame is sent in each beacon period and to minimize actual collisions of the transmitted Beacon frames on the medium, each station in the BSS will choose a random delay value which it will allow to expire after the TBTT before it attempts its Beacon transmission. If the station receives a Beacon from another station in the BSS before the delay expires, the receiving station's Beacon transmission will be cancelled. If, however, the delay expires with the station receiving a Beacon, the Beacon transmission will proceed. It is easy to see that more than one transmission may occur simultaneously, causing corruption of the transmission for some receivers and good reception for others. Thus, some receivers may receive more than one Beacon in a single beacon period. This operation is allowed in the standard and does not cause any degradation or confusion in the receiving stations.

Beaconing also interacts with power management in the independent BSS. The standard requires that the station, or stations, that send a Beacon frame must not enter the power save state until they receive a Beacon frame from another station in the BSS. This restriction on the beaconing station is to ensure that there is at least one station in the IBSS awake and able to respond to probe request frames.

Since each station will send its own value for the TSF timer in the Beacon frames it transmits, the rules for updating the TSF timer in a station in an IBSS are slightly more complex than those for stations in an infrastructure BSS. In an IBSS, a station will update its TSF timer with the value of a received Beacon frame if the received value, after modifying it for processing times, is greater than the value currently in the timer. If the received value is not greater than the local timer value, the received value is discarded. The effect of this selective updating of the TSF timer and the distributed nature of beaconing in an independent BSS is to spread the value of the TSF timer of the station with the fastest running clock throughout the BSS. The speed with which the fastest timer value spreads is dependent on the number of stations in the BSS and whether all stations are able to communicate directly. If the number of stations is small and all stations can communicate directly, the timers of all stations will be updated with the fastest timer value with a period proportional to the number of stations in the BSS. As the number of stations grows and collision of Beacon transmissions occurs, the spread of the fastest timer value will slow. Similarly if all stations cannot communicate directly, it requires more than one station to propagate the fastest timer value to the outlying reaches of the BSS. Thus, the spread of the fastest timer value slows proportional to the number of hops it must take to reach all stations.

Synchronization with Frequency Hopping PHY Layers

The MAC provides the capability to support frequency hopping PHY layers through its synchronization mechanism. Similar to beaconing, changes in a frequency hopping PHY layer (movements to other channels) occurs periodically (the dwell period). With the TSF timers of all stations roughly synchronized, all stations in a BSS will make these changes simultaneously, minimizing the time that could be lost during resynchronization. In particular, all stations in a BSS will change to the new channel when the TSF timer value, modulo the dwell period, is zero.

Scanning

In order for a mobile station to communicate with other mobile stations in an IBSS or with the AP in an infrastructure BSS, it must first find the stations or APs. The process of finding another station or AP is scanning. Scanning may be either passive or active. Passive scanning involves only listening for IEEE 802.11 traffic. Active scanning requires the scanning station to transmit and elicit responses from IEEE 802.11 stations and APs. Both methods are described in the standard. The use of one method or the other is left to the implementer.

Passive scanning allows a mobile station to find a BSS while minimizing the power expended. It does this by not transmitting, only listening. The process a station uses for passive scanning is to move to a channel and listen for Beacon and probe response frames, extracting a description of a BSS from each of these frames received. After a period of time, the station changes to a different channel and listens again. At the conclusion of the passive scan, which may involve listening to one or more channels, the station has accumulated information about the BSSs that are in its vicinity. Though this scanning method may reduce the power expended by the station while scanning, the cost is the additional time required to listen for frames that may not occur, because there is no BSS on the current channel.

Active scanning allows a mobile station to find a BSS while minimizing the time spent scanning. The station does this by actively transmitting queries that elicit responses from stations in a BSS. In an active scan, the mobile station will move to a channel and transmit a probe request frame. If there is a BSS on the channel that matches the SSID in the probe request frame, the station in that BSS that sent the latest Beacon frame will respond by sending a probe response frame to the scanning station. This is the AP in an infrastructure BSS and the last station to send a Beacon in an IBSS. The probe response includes the information necessary for the scanning station to extract a description of the BSS. The scanning station will also process any gratuitously received probe response and Beacon frames. Once the scanning station has processed any responses, or has decided there will be no responses, it may change to another channel and repeat the process. At the conclusion of the scan, the station has accumulated information about the BSSs in its vicinity.

Though the IEEE 802.11 standard describes both active and passive scanning, it does not state any requirements on when each method is to be used. Thus, vendors of IEEE 802.11 equipment are free to innovate and create their own policies regarding the use of active and passive scanning. Some methods that may be seen are to begin a scan with active scanning to rapidly find any IEEE 802.11 WLAN in the vicinity and to revert to passive scanning to conserve power, if the active scan is not successful.

Joining a BSS

Once a station has performed a scan that results in one or more BSS descriptions, the station may choose to join one of the BSSs. The joining process is a purely local process that occurs entirely internal to the IEEE 802.11 mobile station. There is no indication to the outside world that a station has joined a particular BSS. While the IEEE 802.11 standard does describe what is required of a station to join a BSS, it does not describe how a station should choose one BSS over another.

Joining a BSS requires that all of the mobile station's MAC and PHY parameters be synchronized with the desired BSS. To do this, the station must update its TSF timer with the value of the timer from the BSS description, modified by adding the time elapsed since the description was acquired. This will synchronize the TSF timer to the BSS. It will also, coincidentally, synchronize the hopping of frequency hopping PHY layers. The station must also adopt the PHY parameters in the FH parameter set and/or the DS parameter set, as well as the required data rates. This will ensure that the PHY layer is operating on the same channel as that of the rest of the stations in the BSS. The BSSID of the BSS must be adopted, as well as the parameters in the capability information field, such as WEP and the IEEE 802.11b high rate PHY capabilities. The beacon period and DTIM period must also be adopted. Once this process is complete, the mobile station has joined the BSS and is ready to begin communicating with the stations in the BSS.

Combining Management Tools

The MAC management tools described need not be used in isolation. They are most powerful when used in combination.

Combine Power Saving Periods with Scanning

One of the most useful combinations of MAC management tools is combining power saving and scanning in an infrastructure network. With this combination, a mobile station would complete the frame handshake with its AP to inform the AP that the station would be entering the power saving mode. The AP would then begin buffering any arriving data frames for the mobile station. Then, instead of entering the power saving mode, the mobile station would perform active or passive scanning for a period of time, gathering BSS descriptions of other BSSs in the vicinity. The mobile station would then rejoin the BSS where it is associated before either the DTIM approached or the number of beacon periods elapsed, when the AP might begin discarding frames buffered for the mobile station.

This combination allows a mobile station to gather information about its environment, the other BSSs that are nearby, while it has the luxury of being associated and in communication with an AP. This is a much better time to perform this operation than after communication with the AP is lost. Then, when the mobile station eventually does move out of communication with its AP, it has all of the information available to it that will allow it to quickly verify that communication with one of the other BSSs is possible and then to authenticate and reassociate with the new BSS. This minimizes the disruption of communication when it is necessary for a mobile station to roam from one BSS to another.

Preauthentication

Another useful combination of MAC management tools provides preauthentication. Here a mobile station combines scanning with authentication. As the mobile station scans for other BSSs, it will initiate an authentication when it finds a new BSS. This also reduces the time required for a station to resume communication with a new BSS, once it loses communication with the BSS with which it was associated. Now, when communication with the current BSS is no longer satisfactory, the mobile station can join the new BSS and simply reassociate with the AP. The authentication was completed while the mobile station was scanning, some time in the past. It should be noted that some vendors may choose to propagate an station's authentication from one AP to another through the DS, obviating the need for more than a single, initial authentication. The IEEE 802.11 standard does not discuss this operation, nor does it prohibit it.

Chapter 5
MAC Management Information Base

The IEEE 802.11 management information base (MIB) is an SMNPv2 managed object that contains a number of configuration controls, option selectors, counters, and status indicators that allow an external management agent to determine the status and configuration of an IEEE 802.11 station, as well as to probe its performance and tune its operation. The MIB in a station comprises two major sections, one for the MAC and one for the PHY. The PHY section is subdivided into pieces that are specific to each PHY layer. In the MIB definition, there is also a compliance section that describes the required portions of the MIB and those parts that are optional. All of the attributes are arranged in tables, coordinating the attributes that are related to a single function.

The MAC MIB comprises two sections: the station management attributes and the MAC attributes. The station management attributes are associated with the configuration of options in the MAC and the operation of MAC management. The MAC attributes are associated with the operation of the MAC and its performance.

Station Management Attributes

The station management attributes configure and control the operation of the options of the IEEE 802.11 MAC, as well as assist in the management of the station.

dot11StationID is a 48-bit attribute that is designed to allow an external manager to assign its own identifier to a station, for the sole purpose of managing the station. This attribute does not change the actual MAC address of the station. Its default value is the unique MAC address of the station.

The dot11MediumOccupancyLimit attribute provides a limit to the amount of time that the PC may control access to the medium. After this limit is reached, the PC must relinquish control of the medium to the DCF, allowing at least enough time to transmit a single maximum-length MPDU, with fragmentation, before taking control of the medium again. The units used by this attribute are the TU, or 1024 μs. The default value of this attribute is 100 TU. The maximum value is 1000 TU, or 1.024 s. This attribute may be changed by an external manager to allocate more, or less, bandwidth to the PC.

The dot11CFPollable attribute is a Boolean flag that indicates the capability of the station to respond to the CF-Poll frame. This attribute is read-only. It may not be changed by an external manager.

The dot11CFPPeriod attribute defines the length of the CFP, in units of the DTIM interval, which, in turn is in units of the beacon period, that is measured in TU. Thus, to determine the time value of the CFP, multiply the value of this attribute by the DTIM interval (found in the Beacon frame) and multiply the result by 1024 μs. This calculation shows the relationship between beacons, DTIMs, and the CFP.

dot11CFPMaxDuration would appear to have an identical function to dot11MediumOccupancyLimit. However, this attribute is modified by the MLME-Start.request primitive that is used to initiate a BSS. There seems to be no reason for the difference in the maximum allowable values for this attribute and dot11MediumOccupancyLimit.

The dot11AuthenticationResponseTimeout attribute places an upper limit, in TU, on the time a station is allowed before the next frame in an authentication sequence is determined not to be forthcoming. When this timeout expires, the authentication is judged to have failed.

dot11PrivacyOptionImplemented is a Boolean indicator of the presence of the privacy option. This attribute simply indicates that the option is implemented. It does not indicate whether WEP is in use.

dot11PowerManagementMode indicates the state of power management in the station. This attribute is very likely to indicate to an external manager that the station is always in the active mode, never in the power saving mode. This is because the station must be in the active mode to receive a frame from the external manager. Unless a significant time delay occurs between the reception of the frame, the station is likely still to be in the active mode. While this attribute may not be useful to an external manager, a local manager can determine the ratio of active to power saving time in a station through polling this attribute.

dot11DesiredSSID indicates the SSID used during the latest scan operation by the station. Normally, the value of this attribute will be the same as the SSID of the IEEE 802.11 WLAN with which the station is associated. An external manager may change this value, should it be desirable for the station to begin looking for a different WLAN.

dot11DesiredBSSType indicates the type of BSS that the station sought during the latest scan operation. This attribute may be set by an external manager to force scanning for a particular BSS type.

dot11OperationalRateSet is a list of data rates that may be used by the station to transmit in the BSS with which it is associated. The station must also support reception at the rates indicated in this attribute. The rates in this attribute are a subset of those in the dot11SupportedRates in the PHY section of the MIB.

dot11BeaconPeriod controls the time that elapses between target beacon transmission times. This attribute is set by the MLME-Start.request primitive. It may be changed by an external manager. However, any change to this attribute will require that any current BSS be dissolved and a new BSS started with the new beacon period. There is no provision in the standard to gracefully change the beacon period once the BSS has been established.

dot11DTIMPeriod controls the number of beacon periods that elapse between DTIMs. This attribute is also set by the MLME-Start.request primitive. While it may be changed by an external manager, any change will be ineffective until the current BSS is dissolved and a new BSS is started.

The dot11AssociationResponseTimeout attribute places an upper limit on the amount of time that a station will wait for a response to its association request. If an association response is not received before the timeout expires, the request is judged to have failed.

dot11DisassociateReason indicates the reason code received in the most recently received disassociation frame. In combination with dot11DisassociateStation, an external manager can track the location and reasons that stations are disassociated from the WLAN. The dot11DeauthenticateReason and dot11DeauthenticateStation are used similarly to track deauthentications in the WLAN. dot11AuthenticateFailReason and dot11AuthenticateFailStation provide similar information about failures during the authentication process. If a large number of stations are indicating authentication failures, deauthentications, or disassociations, this may be an indication that an AP is misbehaving or that an attack is in progress against the WLAN.

dot11AuthenticationAlgorithm is an entry in a table that holds an entry for each authentication algorithm supported by the station. Every station must support the open system algorithm. If the station also supports the shared key algorithm, the table will hold an entry for that algorithm. Corresponding to each algorithm entry in the table is the dot11AuthenticationAlgorithmsEnable attribute. This attribute indicates whether the associated authentication algorithm is enabled, i.e., if it may be used for authentication by this station.

dot11WEPDefaultKeyValue is an attribute holding one of the WEP default keys. There may be as many as four default keys in a table in the station. This attribute is intended to be write-only. The standard specifies that reading this attribute shall return a value of zero or null.

There is a table of attributes for the WEP key mapping keys. This table holds three accessible attributes: dot11KeyMappingAddress, dot11KeyMappingWEPOn, and dot11KeyMappingValue.

dot11KeyMappingAddress holds the MAC address of a station with which there exists a key mapping relationship. dot11KeyMappingWEPOn is a Boolean value and indicates whether the key mapping key is to be used when communicating with the station with the corresponding address. dot11KeyMappingValue is the key to be used when key mapping is used to communicate with the station with the corresponding address. There is one entry in the key mapping table, consisting of these three attributes, for each station for which a key mapping relationship exists.

dot11PrivacyInvoked is a Boolean attribute that indicates when WEP is to be used to protect data frames. When true, all data frames are to be encrypted using either a default key or a key mapping key before they are transmitted. This value may be changed by an external manager.

dot11WEPDefaultKeyID identifies which of the four default keys are to be used when encrypting data frames with a default key. Choosing a default key to be used for which a corresponding value has not been set will result in an error being returned to higher layer protocols indicating that an attempt was made to encrypt with a null key.

dot11WEPKeyMappingLength indicates the number of entries that may be held in the key mapping table. The minimum value for this attribute is 10, indicating that the key mapping table must hold at least 10 entries.

dot11ExcludeUnencrypted is a Boolean attribute that controls whether a station will receive unencrypted data frames. When this attribute is true, only received data frames that were encrypted will be indicated to higher layer protocols. Unencrypted data frames will be discarded. When an unencrypted data frame is discarded, the value of dot11WEPExcludedCount is incremented. If the dot11WEPExcludedCount is increasing rapidly, it may be due to a station that is misconfigured, attempting to exchange frames without encryption.

The dot11WEPICVErrorCount attribute tracks the number of encrypted frames that have been received and decrypted, but for which the ICV indicates the decryption was not successful. This counter can indicate when an excessive number of decryption errors are encountered. This may be due to a failure to use the same key as that with which the message was encrypted, possibly due to a key update that was missed.

The station management portion of the MIB also includes three notification objects, corresponding to three occurrences that are usually exceptional. The dot11Disassociate object is activated when a station receives a disassociation frame. The dot11Deauthenticate object is activated when the station receives a deauthentication frame. The dot11AuthenticateFail object is activated when the station does not complete an authentication sequence successfully. Each of these notifications can be useful to both local and remote management agents.

MAC Attributes

The MAC attributes tune the performance of the MAC protocol, monitor the performance of the MAC, identify the multicast addresses that the MAC will receive, and provide identification of the MAC implementation.

dot11MACAddress is the unique, individual address of the MAC. It is this address that the MAC considers to be its own and for which it will pass received frames to higher layer protocols. The default for this address is the manufacturer-assigned, globally administered 48-bit MAC address. This attribute may be changed by a local or external manager.

dot11RTSThreshold controls the transmission of RTS control frames prior to data and management frames. The value of this attribute defines the length of the smallest frame for which the transmission of RTS is required. Frames of a length less than the value of this attribute will not be preceded by RTS. The default value of this attribute is 2347, effectively turning off the transmission of RTS for all frames. This attribute may be changed by a local or external manager should it be desirable to enable the transmission of RTS. The IEEE 802.11 standard does not provide any guidelines for when to modify this attribute. However, if the MAC counters indicating frame errors and retransmissions are increasing rapidly, enabling RTS may address this.

dot11ShortRetryLimit controls the number of times a frame that is shorter than the dot11RTSThreshold will be transmitted without receiving an acknowledgment before that frame is abandoned and a failure is indicated to higher layer protocols. The default value of this attribute is 7. It may be modified by local and external managers.

dot11LongRetryLimit controls the number of times a frame that is equal to or longer than the dot11RTSThreshold will be transmitted without receiving an acknowledgment before that frame is abandoned and a failure is indicated to higher layer protocols. The default value of this attribute is 4. It may be modified by local and external managers.

The dot11FragmentationThreshold attribute defines the length of the largest frame that the PHY will accept. Frames larger than this threshold must be fragmented. The default value of this attribute is dependent on the PHY layer parameter aMPDUMaxLength. If the value of aMPDU-MaxLength is greater than or equal to 2346, the default value is 2346. If the value of aMPDUMaxLength is less than 2346, the default value is aMPDUMaxLength. The value of this attribute tracks the value of aMP-DUMaxLength. If aMPDUMaxLength becomes less than the value of this attribute during operation of the station, this attribute will be set to the value of aMPDUMaxLength. This attribute may be modified by local and external managers, but may never exceed the value of aMP-DUMaxLength.

dot11MaxTransmitMSDULifetime controls the length of time that attempts to transmit an MSDU will continue after the initial transmission attempt. Because a frame may be fragmented and the retry limits apply to only a single frame of the fragment stream, this timer limits the amount of bandwidth that may be consumed attempting to deliver a single

MSDU. The value of this attribute is in TU. The default value is 512, or approximately 524 ms. This attribute may be modified by local and external managers.

dot11MaxReceiveLifetime controls the length of time that a partial fragment stream will be held pending reception of the remaining fragments necessary for complete reassembly of the MSDU. If the entire set of fragments has not been received before the lifetime expires, the fragments already received will be discarded. The default value of this attribute, measured in TU, is 512. The value of this attribute may be modified by local and external managers.

dot11ManufacturerID is a variable length character string that identifies the manufacturer of the MAC. This attribute may contain other information, at the manufacturer's discretion, up to the maximum of 128 characters.

dot11ProductID is a variable length character string that identifies the MAC. This attribute may contain other information, at the manufacturer's discretion, up to the maximum of 128 characters.

The dot11TransmittedFragmentCount is a counter that tracks the number of successfully transmitted fragments. As far as this counter is concerned, an MSDU that fits in a single frame without fragmentation is also considered a fragment and will increment this counter. A successful transmission is an acknowledged data frame to an individual address or any data or management frame sent to a multicast address.

The dot11MulticastTransmittedFrameCount is a counter that tracks only transmitted multicast frames. This counter is incremented for every frame transmitted with the group bit set in the destination MAC address.

The dot11FailedCount is a counter that tracks the number of frame transmissions that are abandoned because they have exceeded either the dot11ShortRetryLimit or dot11LongRetyLimit. This counter, along with the retry and multiple retry counters can provide an indication of the "condition" of a BSS. As the load in a BSS increases or the error rate of the medium increases, these counters will increment more rapidly.

The dot11RetryCount is a counter that tracks the number of frames that required at least one retransmission before being delivered successfully. The dot11MultipleRetryCount is a counter that tracks the number of frames that required more than one retransmission to be delivered successfully.

These first five counters can provide additional counter information. The number of individually addressed frames transmitted is equal to dot11MulticastTransmittedFrameCount subtracted from dot11TransmittedFragementCount. The number of frames delivered successfully after only one retransmission is equal to dot11MultipleRetryCount subtracted from dot11RetryCount. The number of frames delivered successfully on the first transmission attempt is equal to dot11RetryCount subtracted from the number of individually addressed frames transmitted.

The dot11FrameDuplicateCount is a counter that tracks the number of duplicate frames received. The value of this counter is indicative of the number of acknowledgments that failed to be delivered.

dot11RTSSuccessCount is a counter that increments for each CTS received in response to an RTS. dot11RTSFailureCount is a counter that increments each time a CTS is not received in response to an RTS.

The dot11ACKFailureCount is a counter that tracks the number of times a data or management frame is sent to an individual address and does not result in the reception of an ACK frame from the destination.

The dot11ReceivedFragmentCount is a counter that tracks the number of fragments received. A fragment is any received frame of type data or management, for the purpose of this counter.

The dot11MulticastReceivedCount is a counter that tracks the number of frames received by the station that match a multicast address in the group addresses table or were sent to the broadcast address.

The dot11FCSErrorCount is a counter that tracks the number of frames received, of any type, that resulted in an FCS error. This counter provides another indication of the "condition" of the BSS. Increasing load and increasing error rate will both result in this counter increasing more rapidly.

dot11TransmittedFrameCount is a counter that tracks the number of MSDUs that have been transmitted successfully. This counter increments only if the entire fragment stream required to transmit an MSDU is sent and an acknowledgment is received for every fragment.

The dot11WEPUndecryptableCount is a counter that tracks the number of frames received without FCS errors and with the WEP bit indicating that the frame is encrypted, but that can not be decrypted due to the dot11WEPOn indicating a key mapping key is not valid or the station not implementing WEP. When this counter increments, it indicates either that the receiving station is misconfigured, has somehow gotten into a BSS that requires WEP, or has missed a key update for a key mapping station.

Multicast addresses for which the station will receive the frame and indicate it to higher layer protocols are stored in an instance of the dot11Address attribute. This attribute is one entry in the dot11GroupAddressesTable. The table is dynamic and entries may be added to and deleted from the table at any time.

The dot11ResourceTypeIDName is an attribute required by IEEE 802.1F. It is a read-only, fixed-length character string. Its default value is "RTID."

The dot11ResourceInfoTable contains four more attributes required by IEEE 802.1F. These attributes are dot11manufacturerOUI, dot11manufacturerName, dot11manufacturerProductName, and dot11manufacturerProductVersion. All of these attributes are read-only. The dot11manufacturerOUI contains the IEEE-assigned 24-bit organizational unique identifier that forms half of a globally administered MAC address. The dot11manufacturerName is a variable length character string containing the name of the manufacturer of the MAC. The dot11manufacturerProductName is also a variable length character string containing the product identifying information for the MAC. The dot11manufacturerProductVersion is also a variable length character string that identifies the version information for the MAC.

Chapter 6
The Physical Layer

Physical Layer (PHY) Functionality

At the bottom of the OSI stack is the PHY (see Figure 6-1). The PHY is the interface between the MAC and wireless media, which transmits and receives data frames over a shared wireless media. The PHY provides three levels of functionality. First, the PHY layer provides a frame exchange between the MAC and PHY under the control of the physical layer convergence procedure (PLCP) sublayer. Secondly, the PHY uses signal carrier and spread spectrum modulation to transmit data frames over the media under the control of the physical medium dependent (PMD) sublayer. Thirdly, the PHY provides a carrier sense indication back to the MAC to verify activity on the media.

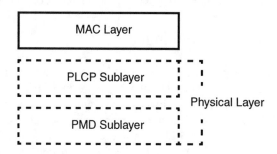

Figure 6-1 — The OSI Model

Each of the PHYs is unique in terms of modulation type and designed to coexist with each other and operate with the MAC described in Chapter 3. While developing the standard, the specifications for IEEE 802.11 were selected to meet the radio frequency (RF) emissions guidelines specified by the Federal Communications Commission (FCC),

European Telecommunications Standards Institute (ETSI), and Ministry of Telecommunications (MKK). This chapter provides an overview and gives the reader a basic understanding of the key specifications for each PHY layer.

Direct Sequence Spread Spectrum (DSSS) PHY

The DSSS PHY is one of the three PHY layers supported in the standard and uses the 2.4 GHz frequency band as the RF transmission media. Data transmission over the media is controlled by the DSSS PMD sublayer as directed by the DSSS PLCP sublayer. The DSSS PMD takes the binary bits of information from the PLCP protocol data unit (PPDU) and transforms them into RF signals for the wireless media by using carrier modulation and DSSS techniques. Figure 6-2 illustrates the basic of elements of the DSSS PMD transmitter and receiver. Details are expanded upon in the subsequent section.

DSSS PLCP Sublayer

The PLCP protocol data unit (PPDU) is unique to the DSSS PHY layer. The PPDU frame consists of a PLCP preamble, PLCP header, and MAC protocol data unit (MPDU) (see Figure 6-3). The receiver uses the PLCP preamble to acquire the incoming signal and synchronize the demodulator. The PLCP header contains information about MPDU from the sending DSSS PHY. The PLCP preamble and PLCP header are always transmitted at 1 Mbps, and the MPDU can be sent at 1 Mbps or 2 Mbps.

SYNC: This field is 128 bits (symbols) in length and contains a string of 1s which are scrambled prior to transmission. The receiver uses this field to acquire the incoming signal and synchronize the receiver's carrier tracking and timing prior to receiving the start of frame delimiter (SFD).

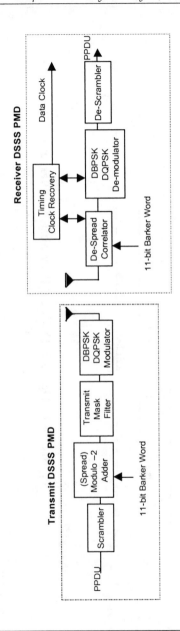

Figure 6-2—Transmit and Receive DSSS PMD

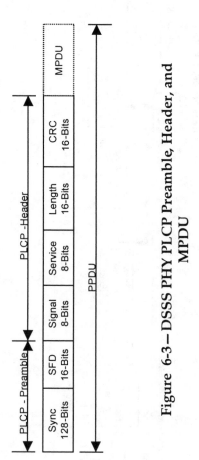

Figure 6-3 – DSSS PHY PLCP Preamble, Header, and MPDU

Start of frame delimiter (SFD): This field contains information marking the start of a PPDU frame. The SFD specified is common for all IEEE 802.11 DSSS radios and uses the following hexadecimal word: F3A0hex.

Signal: The signal field defines which type of modulation must be used to receive the incoming MPDU. The binary value in this field is equal to the data rate multiplied by 100 kbit/s. In the June 1997 version of IEEE 802.11, two rates are supported. They are: 0Ah for 1 Mbps DBPSK and 14hex for 2 Mbps DQPSK.

Service: The service field is reserved future use. However, the default value is 00h.

Length: The length field is an unsigned 16-bit integer that indicates the number of microseconds necessary to transmit the MPDU. The MAC layer uses this field to determine the end of a PPDU frame.

CRC: The CRC field contains the results of a calculated frame check sequence from the sending station. The calculation is performed prior to data scrambling. The CCITT CRC-16 error detection algorithm is used to protect the signal, service and length fields. The CRC-16 algorithm is represent by the following polynomial: $G(x) = x^{16} + x^{12} + x^5 + 1$. The receiver performs the calculation on the incoming signal, service, and length fields and compares the results against the transmitted value. If an error is detected, the receiver's MAC makes the decision if incoming PPDU should be terminated.

Embedded at the end of the MPDU portion of the PPDU is a field called FCS. This field contains a 32-bit CRC, which protects the information in the PLCP service data unit (PSDU). The DSSS PHY does not determine if errors are present in the MPDU. The MAC makes that determination similar to the method used by the PHY layer.

Data Scrambling

All information bits transmitted by the DSSS PMD are scrambled using a self-synchronizing 7-bit polynomial. The scrambling polynomial for the DSSS PHY is: $G(z) = z^{-7} + z^{-4} + 1$. Scrambling is used to randomize the data in the SYNC field of the PLCP and data patterns which contain long strings of binary 1s or 0s. The receiver can descramble the information bits without prior knowledge from the sending station.

DSSS Modulation

In the June 1997 version of IEEE 802.11, the DSSS PMD uses differential phase shift keying (DPSK) as the modulation to transmit the PPDU. Two flavors of DPSK are specified. The DSSS PMD transmits the PLCP preamble and PLCP header 1 Mbps using differential binary phase shift keying (DBPSK). The MPDU is sent at either 1 Mbps DBPSK or 2 Mbps differential quadrature phase shift keying (DQPSK), depending upon the content in the signal field of the PLCP header.

DPSK is a modulation technique which uses a balance inphase/quadrature (I/Q) modulator to generate a RF carrier. The RF carrier is phase modulated carrying symbols mapped from the binary bits in the PPDU. The symbols contain PPDU information. At the receiving station, data recovery for DPSK is based on the phase differences between two consecutive symbols from the sending station. DPSK is noncoherent; a clock reference is not needed to recover the data. For 1 Mbps DBPSK, 1 and 0 binary bits in the PPDU constitute phase shifts of a 180 degrees and the signal information is contained on the I arm. For 2 Mbps DQPSK, two binary bits are combined from the PPDU, generating the following I/Q symbol pairs (00, 01, 11, 00). The phase shifts occur at 90 degrees for DQPSK, as shown in constellation patterns in Figure 6-4. DQPSK could be thought of as transmitting two 1Mbps DBPSK signals, one on the I, the other on the Q. DBPSK is more tolerant to intersymbol interference caused by noise and multipath over the media; therefore DBPSK is used for the PLCP preamble.

For IEEE 802.11-compliant DSSS products, the rotation of DBPSK and DQPSK modulated symbols spinning about the I/Q constellation is counterclockwise. This is noteworthy because it is common to develop DSSS WLAN products that rotate in the opposite direction. The spinning rotation is illustrated in Figure 6-4.

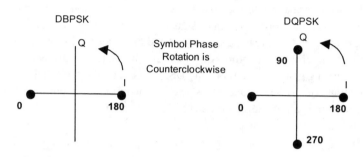

Figure 6-4 — Constellation Patterns for DBPSK and

Barker Spreading Method

The DSSS PHY layer is one of the two 2.4 GHz RF PHY layers to choose from in the IEEE 802.11 standard. Direct Sequence is the spreading method used. An 11-bit Barker word is used as the spreading sequence and every station in an IEEE 802.11 network uses the same 11-bit sequence. Barker word is classified as short sequences and is known to have very good correlation properties.

Barker word (11-bits) +1, −1, +1, +1, −1, +1, +1, +1, −1, −1, −1

In the transmitter, the 11-bit Barker word is applied to a modulo-2 adder (Ex-Or function) together with each of the information bits in the (scrambled) PPDU, as shown in Figure 6-5. The PPDU is clocked at the information rate, 1 Mbps for example, and the 11-Barker word at 11Mbps (the chipping clock). The Ex-Or function combines both signals by performing a modulo-2 addition on each PPDU bit along with each bit (sometimes referred to as a chip) of the Barker word. The output of the modulo-2 adder results in a signal with a data rate that is 10x higher than the information rate. The result in the frequency domain is a signal that is spread over a wider bandwidth at a reduced RF power level. At the receiver, the DSSS signal is convolved with the 11-bit Barker word and correlated. The correlation operation recovers the PPDU information bits at the transmitted information rate, and the undesired interfering in-band signals are spread out-of-band. The spreading and despreading of narrowband to a wideband signal is commonly referred to as processing gain and measured in decibels (dB). Processing gain is the ratio of the DSSS signal rate to the PPDU information rate. The FCC and MKK specify the minimum requirement for processing gain in North America and Japan as 10 dB.

The Barker word used in IEEE 802.11 is not to be confused with the spreading codes used in code division multiple access (CDMA) and global positioning system (GPS). CDMA and GPS use orthogonal spreading codes, which allow multiple users to operate on the same channel frequency. CDMA codes have longer sequences and have richer correlation properties.

DSSS Operating Channels and Transmit Power Requirements

Each DSSS PHY channel occupies 22 MHz of bandwidth, and the spectral shape of the channel represents a filtered SinX/X function (see Figure 6-6). The DS channel transmit mask in IEEE 802.11 specifies that spectral products be filtered to –30dBr from the center frequency and all other products be filtered to –50dBr. This allows for three noninterfering channels spaced 25 MHz apart in the 2.4 GHz frequency band. For example, the channel, arrangement for North America is illustrated in Figure 6-7). With this channel arrangement, a user can configure multiple DSSS networks to operate simultaneously in the same area.

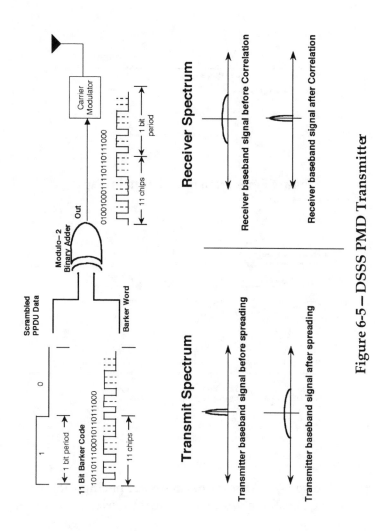

Figure 6-5 – DSSS PMD Transmitter

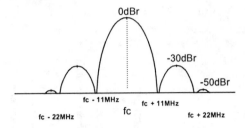

Figure 6-6—Transmit Channel Shape

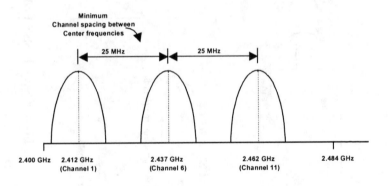

Figure 6-7—Minimum Channel Spacing for DSSS Networks in North America

In IEEE 802.11 fourteen center frequency channels are defined for operation across the 2.4 GHz frequency band (see Table 6-1). In North America 12 channels are allowed ranging from 2.412 GHz to 2.462 GHz. In most of Europe thirteen channels are allowed ranging from 2.412 GHz to 2.472 GHz and in Japan one channel frequency is reserved at 2.483 GHz.

Table 6-1—DSSS Channels for Various Parts of the Globe

Channel Number	Frequency GHz	North America	Europe	Spain	France	Japan-MKK
1	2.412	X	X			
2	2.417	X	X			
3	2.422	X	X			
4	2.427	X	X			
5	2.432	X	X			
6	2.437	X	X			
7	2.442	X	X			
8	2.447	X	X			
9	2.452	X	X			
10	2.457	X	X	X	X	
11	2.462	X	X	X	X	
12	2.467		X		X	
13	2.472		X		X	
14	2.483					X

In addition to frequency and bandwidth allocations, transmit power is a key parameter that is regulated worldwide. The maximum allowable radiated emissions for the DSSS PHY varies from region to region, as illustrated in Table 6-2. The transmit power is directly related to the range a particular IEEE 802.11 DSSS PHY implementation can achieve. Many of the IEEE 802.11 DSSS PHY wireless products on the market today have selected 100 mW as the nominal RF transmit power level.

Table 6-2 — Maximum Allowable Transmit Power Worldwide

1000 mW	North America
100 mW	Europe
10 mW/MHz	Japan

The Frequency Hopping Spread Spectrum (FHSS) PHY

As with the DSSS PHY, the FHSS PHY is one of the three PHY layers supported in the standard and uses the 2.4 GHz spectrum as the transmission media. Data transmission over the media is controlled by the FHSS PMD sublayer as directed by the FHSS PLCP sublayer. The FHSS PMD takes the binary bits of information from the whitened PSDU and transforms them into RF signals for the wireless media by using carrier modulation and FHSS techniques. Figure 6-8 illustrates the basic elements of the FHSS PMD transmitter and receiver. Details of each are expanded upon in the subsequent section.

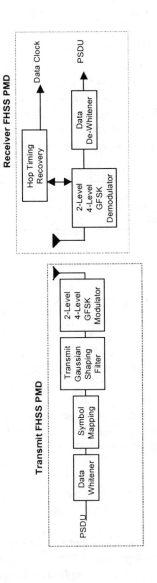

Figure 6-8 — Transmit and Receive FHSS PMD

FHSS PLCP Sublayer

The PLCP preamble, PLCP header, and PLCP service data unit (PSDU) make up the PLCP protocol data unit (PPDU) as shown in Figure 6-9. The PLCP preamble and PLCP header are unique to the FHSS PHY. The PLCP preamble is used to acquire the incoming signal and synchronize the receiver's demodulator. The PLCP header contains information about PSDU from the sending FH PHY. The PLCP preamble and PLCP header are transmitted at 1 Mbps (the basic rate).

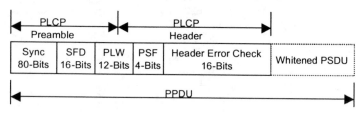

Figure 6-9 — FHSS PHY PLCP Preamble, Header, and PSDU

SYNC: This field contains a string of alternating 0s and 1s patterns and is used by the receiver to synchronize the receiver's packet timing and correct for frequency offsets.

SFD: This field contains information marking the start of a PSDU frame. A common SFD is specified for all IEEE 802.11 FHSS radios using the following bit pattern: 0000110010111101. The left most bit is transmitted first.

PLW: This field specifies the length of the PSDU in octets and is used by the MAC to detect the end of a PPDU frame.

PLCP signaling field (PSF): The PSF identifies the data rate of the whitened PSDU ranging from 1 Mbps to 4.5 Mbps in increments of 0.5 Mbps. (See Table 6-3). The PLCP preamble and header are transmitted at the basic rate, 1 Mbps. The optional data rate for the whitened PSDU is 2 Mbps.

Table 6-3 — PSF Bit Assignments for PSDU Data Rates

Bits 1-3	Data Rates — Mbps
000	1.0
001	1.5
010	2.0
011	2.5
100	3.0
101	3.5
110	4.0
111	4.5

Header check error: This field contains the results of a calculated frame check sequence from the sending station. The calculation is performed prior to data whitening. The CCITT CRC-16 error detection algorithm is used to protect the PSF and PLW fields. The CRC-16 algorithm is represented by the following polynomial: $G(x) = x^{16} + x^{12} + x^5 + 1$. The receiver performs the calculation on the incoming PSF and PLW fields and compares the results against the transmitted field. If an error is detected, the receiver's MAC determines if the incoming PPDU should be terminated.

Embedded at the end of the PSDU portion of the PPDU is a field called FCS. This field contains a 32-bit CRC, which protects the information in the PSDU. The FHSS PHY does not determine if errors are present in the PSDU. The MAC makes that determination, similar to the method used by the PHY.

PSDU Data Whitening

Data whitening is applied to the PSDU before transmission to minimize DC bias on the data if long strings of 1s or 0s are contained in the PSDU. The PHY stuffs a special symbol every 4 octets of the PDSU in a PPDU frame. A 127-bit sequence generator using the polynomial $S(x) = x^7 + x^4 + 1$ and a 32/33 bias-suppression encoding algorithm are used to randomize and whiten the data.

FHSS Modulation

In the June 1997 version of IEEE 802.11, the FHSS PMD uses two-level Gaussian frequency shift key (GFSK) modulation to transmit the PSDU at the basic rate of 1 Mbps. The PLCP preamble and PLCP header are always transmitted at 1 Mbps. However, four-level GFSK is an optional modulation method defined in the standard that enables the whitened PSDU to be transmitted at a higher rate. The value contained in the PSF field of the PLCP header is used to determine the data rate of the PSDU.

GFSK is a modulation technique used by the FHSS PMD, which deviates (shifts) the frequency either side of the carrier hop frequency depending on if the binary symbol from the PSDU is either a 1 or 0. A bandwidth bit period (Bt) = 0.5 is used. The changes in the frequency represent symbols containing PSDU information. For two-level GFSK, a binary 1 represents the upper deviation frequency from the hopped carrier, and a binary 0 represents the lower deviation frequency. The deviation frequency shall be greater than 110 KHz for IEEE 802.11 FHSS radios. The carrier frequency deviation is given by:

Binary 1 = $F_c + f_d$ Carrier hopped frequency plus the upper deviated frequency

Binary 0 = $F_c - f_d$ Carrier hopped frequency minus the lower deviated frequency

Four-level GFSK is similar to two-level GFSK and used to achieve a data rate of 2 Mbps in the same occupied frequency bandwidth. The modulator combines two binary bits from the whitened PSDU and encodes them into symbol pairs (10, 11, 01, 00). The symbol pairs generate four frequency deviations from the hopped carrier frequency, two upper and two lower. The symbol pairs are transmitted at 1 Mbps, and for each bit sent, the resulting data rate is 2 Mbps.

FHSS Channel Hopping

A set of hop sequences is defined in IEEE 802.11 for use in the 2.4 GHz frequency band. The channels are evenly spaced across the band over a span 83.5 MHz. During the development of the IEEE 802.11, the hop sequences listed in the standard were preapproved for operation in North American, Europe, and Japan. The required number of hop channels is dependent upon the geographic location. In North American and Europe (excluding Spain and France) the number of hop channels is 79. The number of hopped channels for Spain is 23 and 35 for France. In Japan the required number of hopped channels is 23. The hopped center channels are spaced uniformly across the 2.4 GHz frequency band occupying a bandwidth of 1 MHz. In North America and Europe (excluding Spain and France) the hopped channels operate from 2.402 GHz to 2.480 GHz and for Japan, 2.473 GHz to 2.495 GHz. In Spain the hopped channels operate from 2.447 GHz to 2.473 GHz, and for France, 2.448 GHz to 2.482 GHz. Channel 2 is the first hopped channel located at center frequency of 2.402 GHz and channel 95 is the last hopped frequency channel in the 2.4 Ghz band centered at 2.495 Ghz.

Channel hopping is controlled by the FHSS PMD. The FHSS PMD transmits the whitened PSDU by hopping from channel to channel in a pseudorandom fashion using one of the hopping sequences. The hop rate is set by the regulatory bodies in the country of operation. In the US, FHSS radios must hop a minimum of 2.5 hops per second for a minimum hop distance of 6 MHz. This is in accordance with the rules specified by the FCC rules under Part 15.

The hopping sequences for IEEE 802.11 are grouped in hopping sets for worldwide operation: Set 1, Set 2, and Set 3. The sequences are selected when a FHSS BSS is configured for a WLAN. The hopping sets are designed to minimize interference between neighboring FHSS radios in a set. The following hop sets are valid IEEE 802.11 hopping sequence numbers.

Operation in North America and most of Europe:

> Set 1: (0, 3, 6, 9, 12, 15, 18, 21, 24, 27, 30, 33, 36, 39,42, 45, 48, 51, 54, 57, 60, 63, 66, 69, 72, 75)
>
> Set 2: (1, 4, 7, 10, 13, 16, 19, 22, 25, 28, 31, 34, 37, 40, 43, 46, 49, 52, 55, 58, 61, 64, 67, 70, 73, 76)
>
> Set 3: (2, 5, 8, 11, 14, 17, 20, 23, 26, 29, 32, 35, 38, 41, 44, 47, 50, 53, 56, 59,62, 65, 68, 72, 74, 77)

Operation in Spain:

> Set 1: (0, 3, 6, 9, 12, 15, 18, 21, 24)
>
> Set 2: (1, 4, 7, 10, 13, 16, 19, 22, 25)
>
> Set 3: (2, 5, 8, 11, 14, 17, 20, 23, 26)

Operation in France:

> Set 1: (0, 3, 6, 9, 12, 15, 18, 21, 24, 27, 30)
>
> Set 2: (1, 4, 7, 10, 13, 16, 19, 22, 25, 28, 31)
>
> Set 3: (2, 5, 8, 11, 14, 17, 20, 23, 26, 29, 32)

Operation in Japan:

> Set 1: (6, 9, 12, 15)
>
> Set 2: (7, 10, 13, 16)
>
> Set 3: (8, 11, 14, 17)

Infrared (IR) PHY

The IR PHY is one of the three PHY layers supported in the standard. The IR PHY differs from DSSS and FHSS because IR uses near-visible light as the transmission media. IR communication relies on light energy, which is reflected off objects or by line-of-sight. The IR PHY operation is restricted to indoor environments and cannot pass through walls, such as DSSS and FHSS radio signals. Data transmission over the media is controlled by the IR PMD sublayer as directed by the IR PLCP sublayer. The IR PMD takes the binary bits of information from the PSDU and transforms them into light energy emissions for the wireless media by using carrier modulation. Figure 6-10 illustrates the basic elements of the FHSS PMD transmitter and receiver. Details of each are expanded upon in the subsequent section.

IR PLCP Sublayer

The PLCP preamble, PLCP header, and PSDU make up the PPDU, as shown in Figure 6-11. The PLCP preamble and PLCP header are unique to the IR PHY. The PLCP preamble is used to acquire the incoming signal and synchronize the receiver prior to the arrival of the PSDU. The PLCP header contains information about PSDU from the sending IR PHY. The PLCP preamble and PLCP header are always transmitted at 1 Mbps and the PSDU can be sent at 1 Mbps or 2 Mbps.

SYNC: This field contains a sequence of alternated presence and absence of a pulse in consecutive time slots. The SYNC field is used by the IR PHY to perform signal acquisition and clock recovery. The standard specifies 57 time slots as the minimum and 73 time slots as the maximum.

SFD: This field contains information that marks the start of a PPDU frame. A common SFD is specified for all IEEE 802.11 IR implementations. The SFD is represented by the following bit pattern: 1001

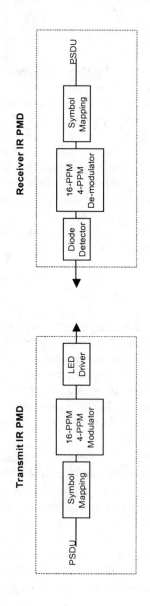

Figure 6-10 — Transmit and Receive IR PMD

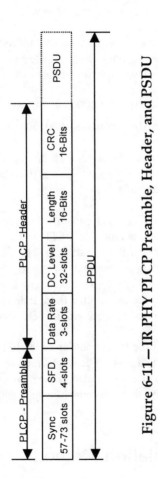

Figure 6-11 — IR PHY PLCP Preamble, Header, and PSDU

Data rate: This field defines the data rate the PPDU is transmitted. There are two rates to choose from 000 for 1 Mbps (the basic rate) and 001 for 2 Mbps (the enhanced access rate). The PLCP preamble and PLCP header are always sent at the basic rate 1 Mbps.

DC level: This field contains information that allows the IR PHY to stabilize the DC level after receiving the preamble and data rate fields. The supported data rates use the following bit patterns:

   1 Mbps: 00000000100000000000000010000000

   2 Mbps: 00100010001000100010001000100010

Length: This field contains an unsigned 16-bit integer that indicates the number of microseconds to transmit the PSDU. The MAC layer uses this field to detect the end of a frame.

Frame check sequence: The field contains the calculated 16-bit CRC result from the sending station. The CCITT CRC-16 error detection algorithm is used to protect the length field. The CRC-16 algorithm is represent by the following polynomial: $G(x) = x^{16} + x^{12} + x^5 + 1$. The receiver performs the calculation on the incoming Length field and compares the results against the transmitted field. If an error is detected, the receiver's MAC determines if the incoming PSDU should be terminated.

Embedded at the end of the PSDU portion of the PPDU is a field called FCS. This field contains a 32-bit CRC, which protects the information in the PSDU. The IR PHY does not determine if errors are present in the PSDU. The MAC makes that determination similar to the method used by the PHY layer.

IR PHY Modulation Method

The IR PHY transmits binary data at 1 and 2 Mbps using a modulation known as pulse position modulation (PPM). PPM is used in IR systems to reduce the optical power required of the LED infrared source. The specific data rate is dependent upon the type of PPM. The modulation for 1 Mbps operation is 16-PPM and 4-PPM for 2 Mbps. PPM is a modulation technique that keeps the amplitude, pulse width constant, and varies the position of the pulse in time. Each position represents a different symbol in time.

For 16-PPM each group of data bits of the PSDU is mapped to one of the 16-PPM symbols for 1 Mbps operation. Notice in Table 6-4 a "1" bit in the 16-PPM symbol represents data bit position. The order of the transmission bits is left to right. The data bits are arranged (gray coded) to reduce the possibility of multiple bit errors due to intersymbol interference in the media.

For 2 Mbps operation 4-PPM is used and two data bits are paired in the PSDU to form a 4-bit symbol map as shown in Table 6-5. The transmission order of the bits is left to right.

Table 6-4—16-PPM Symbol Map for 1 Mbps

Data Bits	16-PPM Symbols
0000	0000000000000001
0001	0000000000000010
0011	0000000000001000
0010	0000000000010000
0110	0000000000100000
0111	0000000001000000
0101	0000000010000000
0100	0000000100000000
1100	0000001000000000
1101	0000010000000000

Table 6-4 — 16-PPM Symbol Map for 1 Mbps (*Continued*)

Data Bits	16-PPM Symbols
1111	00000100000000000
1110	00001000000000000
1010	00010000000000000
1011	00100000000000000
1001	01000000000000000
1000	10000000000000000

Table 6-5 — 4-PPM Symbol Map for 2 Mbps

Data Bits	4-PPM Symbol
00	0001
01	0010
11	0100
10	1000

Geographic Regulatory Bodies

WLAN IEEE 802.11-compliant DSSS and FHSS radios operating in the 2.4 GHz frequency band must comply with the local geographical regulatory domains before operating in this spectrum. These products are subject to certification. The technical requirements in the IEEE 802.11 standard were developed to comply with the regulatory agencies in North America, Europe, and Japan. The regulatory agencies in these regions set emission requirements for WLANs to minimize the amount of interference a radio can generate or receive from another in the same proximity. The regulatory requirements do not affect the interoperability of IEEE 802.11-compliant products. It is the responsibility of the product developers to check with the regulatory agencies. In some cases, additional certifications are necessary for regions within Europe or outside of Japan or North America. Listed below are some agencies defined by IEEE 802.11.

North America

Approval Standards: Industry Canada
Documents: GL36
Approval Authorities: Federal Communications Commission, (FCC)
USA Documents: CFR 47, Part 15 Sections 15.205, 15.209, 15.247
Approval Authority: Industry Canada, FCC (USA)

Spain

Approval Standards: Supplemento Del Numero 164 Del Boletin Oficial Del Estado (Published 10, July 91, Revised 25 June 93)
Documents: ETS 300-328, ETS 300-339
Approval Authority: Cuadro Nacional De Atribucion De Frecuesias

Europe

Approval Standards: European Telecommunications Standards Institute
Documents: ETS 300-328, ETS 300-339
Approval Authority: National Type Approval Authorities

Chapter 7
Physical Layer Extensions to
IEEE 802.11

In October 1997 the IEEE 802 Executive Committee approved two projects to for higher rate physical layer (PHY) extensions to IEEE 802.11. The first extension, IEEE 802.11a, defines requirements for a PHY operating in the 5.0 GHz U-NII frequency and data rates ranging from 6 Mbps to 54 Mbps. The second extension, IEEE 802.11b, defines a set of PHY specifications operating in the 2.4 GHz ISM frequency band up to 11Mbps. Both PHY are defined to operate with the existing MAC. At the time this handbook was written, the draft specifications for IEEE 802.11a and IEEE 802.11b were in the final stages of approval, and vendors' products were starting to emerge in the market. This chapter gives the reader a general overview of some of the requirements specified for each.

IEEE 802.11a — The OFDM Physical Layer

The IEEE 802.11a PHY is one of the physical layer (PHY) extensions of IEEE 802.11 and is referred to as the orthogonal frequency division multiplexing (OFDM) PHY. The OFDM PHY provides the capability to transmit PSDU frames at multiple data rates up to 54 Mbps for WLAN networks where transmission of multimedia content is a consideration. The OFDM PHY defined for IEEE 802.11a is similar to the OFDM PHY specification of ETSI-HIPERLAN II. At the time this book was written, both organizations were in the final stages of agreeing to a common set of specifications.

In the OSI structure, the PHY's PLCP sublayer and PMD sublayer are unique to the OFDM PHY. The following sections give an overview of the PLCP header, data rates, and modulations defined in IEEE 802.11a.

OFDM PLCP Sublayer

The PPDU is unique to the OFDM PHY. The PPDU frame consists of a PLCP preamble and signal and data fields as shown in Figure 7-1. The receiver uses the PLCP preamble to acquire the incoming OFDM signal and synchronize the demodulator. The PLCP header contains information about the PSDU from the sending OFDM PHY. The PLCP preamble and the signal field are always transmitted at 6 Mbps, binary phase shift keying (BPSK)-OFDM modulated using convolutional encoding rate R = 1/2.

PLCP preamble: This field is used to acquire the incoming signal and train and synchronize the receiver. The PLCP preamble consists of 12 symbols, ten of which are short symbols, and two long symbols. The short symbols are used to train the receiver's AGC and obtain a coarse estimate of the carrier frequency and the channel. The long symbols are used to fine-tune the frequency and channel estimates. Twelve subcarriers are used for the short symbols and 53 for the long. The training of an OFDM is accomplished in 16 μs. PLCP preamble is BPSK–OFDM modulated at 6 Mbps.

Signal: The signal is a 24-bit field, which contains information about the rate and length of the PSDU. The Signal field is convolutional encoded rate 1/2, BPSK–OFDM modulated. Four bits (R1-R4) are used to encode the rate, eleven bits are defined for the length, one reserved bit, a parity bit, and six "0" tail bits. The rate bits (R1-R4) are defined in Table 7-1. The mandatory data rates for IEEE 802.11a-compliant systems are 6 Mbps, 12 Mbps, and 24 Mbps.

Length: The length field is an unsigned 12-bit integer that indicates the number of octets in the PSDU.

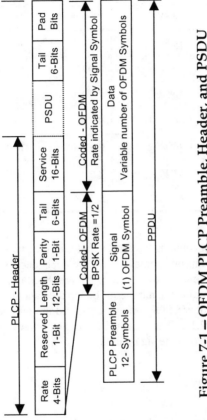

Figure 7-1 — OFDM PLCP Preamble, Header, and PSDU

Table 7-1— PSDU Date Rate Selection

Rate	Modulation	Coding Rate	Signal bits (R1-R4)
6 Mbps	BPSK	R = 1/2	1101
9 Mbps	BPSK	R = 3/4	1111
12 Mbps	QPSK	R = 1/2	0101
18 Mbps	QPSK	R = 3/4	0111
24 Mbps	16QAM	R = 1/2	1001
36 Mbps (optional)	16QAM	R = 3/4	1011
48 Mbps (optional)	64QAM	R = 2/3	0001
54 Mbps (optional)	64QAM	R = 3/4	0011

Data: The data field contains the service field, PSDU, tails bits, and pad bits. A total of six tail bits containing 0s are appended to the PPDU to ensure that the convolutional encoder is brought back to zero state. The equation for determining the number of bits in the data field, the number of tail bits, the number of OFDM symbols, and the number pad bits is defined in IEEE 802.11a. The data portion of the packet is transmitted at the data rate indicated in the signal field.

Data Scrambler

All the bits transmitted by the OFDM PMD in the data portion are scrambled using a frame-synchronous 127-bit sequence generator. Scrambling is used to randomize the service, PSDU, pad bit, and data patterns, which may contain long strings of binary 1s or 0s. The tail bits are not scrambled. The scrambling polynomial for the OFDM PHY is: $S(x) = x^{-7} + x^{-4} + 1$. The initial state of the scrambler is randomly chosen. Prior to scrambling the PPDU frame, the seven least significant bits of the service field are reset to 0 in order to estimate the initial state of the scrambler in the receiver.

Convolutional Encoding

All information contained in the service, PSDU, tail, and pad are encoded using convolutional encoding rate R = 1/2, 2/3, or 3/4 corresponding to the desired data rate. Convolutional encoding is generated using the following polynomials; $g_0 = 133_8$ and $g_1 = 171_8$ of rate R = 1/2. Puncture codes are used for the higher data rates. Industry standard algorithms, such as the Viterbi algorithm, are recommended for decoding.

OFDM Modulation

In July of 1998 the IEEE 802.11 Working Group adopted OFDM modulation as the basis for IEEE 802.11a. This OFDM method chosen is similar to the modulation technique adopted in Europe by ETSI-HIP-ERLAN II 5 GHz radio PHY specification. The basic principal of operation first divides a high-speed binary signal to be transmitted into a number of lower data rate subcarriers. There are 48 data subcarriers and 4 carrier pilot subcarriers for a total of 52 nonzero subcarriers defined in IEEE 802.11a. Each lower data rate bit stream is used to modulate a separate subcarrier from one of the channels in the 5 GHz band. Intersymbol interference is generally not a concern for lower speed carrier, however the subchannels may be subjected to frequency selective fading. Therefore, bit interleaving and convolutional encoding is used to improve the bit error rate performance. The scheme uses integer multiples of the first subcarrier, which are orthogonal to each other. This technique is known as orthogonal frequency division multiplexing (OFDM). Prior to transmission the PPPU is encoded using a convolutional coded rate R = 1/2, and the bits are reordered and bit interleaved for the desired data rate. Each bit is then mapped into a complex number according the modulation type and subdivided in 48 data subcarriers and 4 pilot subcarriers. The subcarriers are combined using an inverse fast fourier transform and transmitted. At the receiver, the carrier is converted back to a multicarrier lower data rate form using an FFT. The lower data subcarriers are combined to form the high rate PPDU. An example of an IEEE 802.11a OFDM PMD is illustrated in Figure 7-2.

OFDM Operating Channels and Transmit Power Requirements

The 5 GHz U-NII frequency band is segmented into three 100 MHz bands for operation in the US. The lower band ranges from 5.15–5.25 GHz, the middle band ranges from 5.25–5.35 GHz and the upper band ranges from 5.725–5.825 GHz. The lower and middle bands accommodate 8 channels in a total bandwidth of 200 MHz and the upper band accommodates 4 channels in a 100 MHz bandwidth. The frequency channels center frequencies are spaced 20 MHz apart. The outermost channels of the lower and middle bands are centered 30 MHz from the outer edges. In the upper band the outermost channel centers are 20 MHz from the outer edges. The channel frequencies and numbering defined in IEEE 802.11a start at 5 GHz and each channel is spaced 5 GHz apart. A set of channel frequencies for each of the U-NII bands is defined in Table 7-2.

In addition to frequency and channel allocations, transmit power is a key parameter regulated in the 5 GHz U-NII frequency band. Three transmit RF power levels are specified; 40 mW, 200 mW and 800 mW as illustrated in Table 7-3. The upper band defines RF transmit power levels suitable for bridging applications while the lower band specifies a transmit power level suitable for short-range indoor home and small office environments.

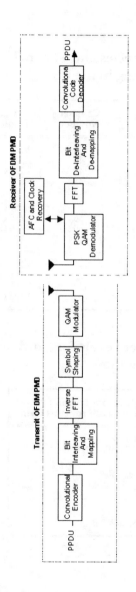

Figure 7-2 — IEEE 802.11a Transmit and Receive OFDM PMD

Table 7-2 — Channel Frequencies and Channel Numbers for Operating in the US

Regulatory Domain	Frequency Band	Channel Number	Center Frequencies
USA	U-NII lower band 5.15–5.25 GHz	36 40 44 48	5.180 GHz 5.220 GHz 5.220 GHz 5.240 GHz
USA	U-NII middle band 5.25–5.35 GHz	52 56 60 64	5.260 GHz 5.280 GHz 5.300 GHz 5.320 GHz
USA	U-NII upper band 5.725–5.825 GHz	149 153 157 161	5.745 GHz 5.765 GHz 5.785 GHz 5.805 GHz

Table 7-3 — Transmit Power Levels for North America Operation

Frequency Band	Maximum Transmit Power with 6 dBi Antenna Gain
5.150 – 5.250 GHz	40 mW (2.5 mW/MHz)
5.250– 5.350 GHz	200 mW (12.5 mW/MHz)
5.725– 5.825 GHz	800 mW (50 mW/MHz)

Geographic Regulatory Bodies

WLAN IEEE 802.11a-compliant OFDM radios operating in the 5 GHz UNII frequency band must comply with the local geographical regulatory domains before operating in this spectrum. These products are subject to certification. At the time IEEE 802.11a was being developed, the technical requirements were specified to comply with the regulatory requirements in North America. The regulatory agencies set emission requirements for WLANs to minimize the amount of interference a radio can generate or receive from another in the same proximity. The regulatory requirements do not affect the interoperability of IEEE 802.11a-compliant products. It is the responsibility of the product developers to check with the regulatory agencies for the necessary certifications. In the US the FCC is responsible for the allocation of 5 GHz U-UNII bands.

North America

Geographic Area: USA
Approval Standards: Federal Communications Commission (FCC)
Documents: CFR47, Part 15; Sections 15.205,15.209, and subpart E; Sections 15.401–15.407
Approval Authorities: Federal Communications Commission (FCC)

Globalization of Spectrum at 5 GHz

At the time, we were writing this book, IEEE 802.11, ETSI's HIPER-LAN II and Japan's Mobile Multimedia Access Communication Promotion Council (MMAC-PC) were pursuing available spectrum allocations in the 5 GHz band. In Europe the 5.15–5.35 GHz frequency band is reserved for HIPERLAN II devices. Discussions were underway between ETSI-HIPERLAN II and IEEE 802.11 to share the lower 5 GHz band as a possibility, drawing on the extreme similarity of the PHY layers of both projects. In Japan the Wireless Ethernet Working Group of the MMAC-PC recommends using the 802.11a standard whenever the 5.15–5.25 GHz band becomes available in Japan.

IEEE 802.11b–2.4 High Rate DSSS PHY

The IEEE 802.11b PHY is one of the PHY layer extensions of IEEE 802.11 and is referred to as high rate direct sequence spread spectrum (HR/DSSS). The HR/DSSS PHY provides two functions. First, the HR/DSSS extends the PSDU data rates to 5.5 Mbps and 11 Mbps using an enhanced modulation technique. Secondly, the HR/DSSS PHY provides a rate shift mechanism, which allows 11 Mbps networks to fall back to 1 and 2 Mbps and interoperate with the legacy IEEE 802.11 2.4 GHz RF PHY layers. The OSI structure and operation of the PHY's PLCP sublayer and PMD sublayer for HR/DSSS is similar to the existing IEEE 802.11 DSSS PHY described in Chapter 6. The following sections give an overview of the PLCP header, data rates, and modulations defined in IEEE 802.11b.

HR/DSSS PHY PLCP Sublayer

A PPDU frame consists of the PLCP preamble, PLCP header, and the PSDU. As with IEEE 802.11 DSSS, the PMD uses the PLCP preamble to acquire the incoming signal and synchronize the receiver's demodulator. The HR/DSSS PHY defines two PLCP preambles, long and short (see Figure 7-3). The long preamble uses the same PLCP preamble and header as the IEEE 802.11 DSSS PHY and sends the information at 1 Mbps using DBPSK and Barker word direct sequence spreading. The PSDU is transmitted at 1, 2, 5.5, and 11 Mbps as determined by the content in the signal field. The long preamble is backwards compatible with existing IEEE 802.11 DSSS PHY and defined to interoperate with existing IEEE 802.11 wireless networks operating at 1 and 2 Mbps.

The short preamble uses a 56-bit SYNC field to acquire the incoming signal, and transmits the preamble at 1 Mbps using DBPSK modulation and Barker word spreading. The PLCP header transmits at 2 Mbps using DQPSK and Barker word spreading (see Figure 7-3) In this case, the PSDU is transmitted at 2, 5.5, or 11 Mbps as determined by the content in the signal field. The short preamble is an option in IEEE 802.11b and is useful for those networks where throughput efficiency and interoperability with existing IEEE 802.11 DSSS radios in not necessary. There is one caveat: the short preamble radio can only interoperate with itself; therefore, for a short preamble radio to be IEEE 802.11b compliant must support the long preamble.

SYNC: The receiver uses this field to acquire the incoming signal and synchronize the receiver's carrier tracking and timing prior to receiving the SFD. The long preamble SYNC field is 128 bits in length containing a string of scrambled 1s. The scrambler seed bit patterned used to initialize the scrambler for the long preamble is 01101100. The short preamble SYNC field is 56 bits in length and contains a string of scrambled 0s. The scrambler seed bit patterned used to initialize the scrambler for short preamble operation is 00011010. The short preamble SYNC field is used for networks where minimizing overhead and maximizing PSDU throughput is a consideration.

SFD: This field contains information marking the start of a PPDU frame. The SFD specified is common for all IEEE 802.11 DSSS and IEEE 802.11b long preamble radios. The following hexadecimal word is used: F3A0hex transmitted LSB first. For short preamble radios, the following hexadecimal word is used: 05CFhex transmitted LSB first.

Signal: The signal field defines which type of modulation must be used to receive the incoming PSDU. The binary value in this field is equal to the data rate multiplied by 100 kbit/s. The 1 Mbps data rate is used for long and short preamble implementations.

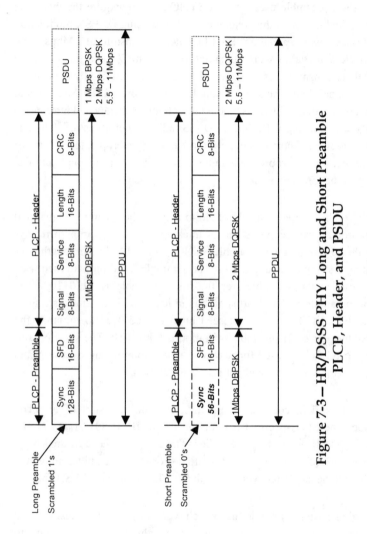

Figure 7-3—HR/DSSS PHY Long and Short Preamble PLCP, Header, and PSDU

The bit patterns in this field always represent the following data rates:

Signal Field	Data Rate
00001010	1 Mbps (long preamble only)
00010100	2 Mbps
00111110	5.5 Mbps
01101110	11 Mbps

Service: The service field uses 3 bits of the reserved 8 bits for IEEE 802.11b. Data bit (b2) determines whether the transmit frequency and symbol clocks use the same local oscillator. Data bit (b3) indicates whether complimentary code keying (CCK) or packet binary convolutional coding (PBCC) is used and data bit (b7) is a bit extension used in conjunction with the length field to calculate the duration of the PSDU in microseconds. This field is used for the long and short preamble frames.

Length: The length field is an unsigned 16-bit integer that indicates the number of microseconds necessary to transmit the PSDU. For any data rate over 8 Mbps, bit-7 of the service field is used with the length field to determine the time in microseconds from the number of octets contained in the length field. A calculation is defined in IEEE 802.11b for determining the length in microseconds for CCK and PBCC as applied to both preambles. The MAC layer uses this field to determine the end of a PPDU frame.

CRC: The CRC field contains the results of a calculated frame check sequence from the sending station. The calculation is performed prior to data scrambling for the long and short preamble. The CCITT CRC-16 error detection algorithm is used to protect the signal, service, and length fields. The CRC-16 algorithm is represent by the following polynomial: $G(x) = x^{16} + x^{12} + x^5 + 1$. The receiver performs the calculation on the incoming Signal, Service and Length field and compares the results against the transmitted value. If an error is detected, the receiver's MAC makes the decision if incoming PSDU should be terminated.

High Rate Data Scrambling

All information bits transmitted by the DSSS PMD are scrambled using a self-synchronizing 7-bit polynomial. The scrambling polynomial for the DSSS PHY is: $G(z) = z^{-7} + z^{-4} + 1$. Scrambling is used to randomize the long and short preamble data in the SYNC field of the PLCP and for data patterns which contain long strings of binary 1s or 0s. The receiver can descramble the information bits without prior knowledge from the sending station. The scrambler initialization bit patterns are represented as (00011010) for the short preamble and (01101100) for the long preamble.

IEEE 802.11 High Rate Operating Channels

The HR/DSSS PHY uses the same frequency channels as defined in Chapter 6 for the IEEE 802.11 direct sequence PHY. The channel center frequencies are spaced 25 MHz apart to allow multiple WLAN systems to operate simultaneously in the same area without interfering with each other. An example of a typical channel arrangement for noninterfering channels for North America is illustrated in Figure 7-4. In Europe the channels 1 (2.412 GHz), 7 (2.442 GHz) and 13 (2.472 GHz) are used to form three non-interfering networks.

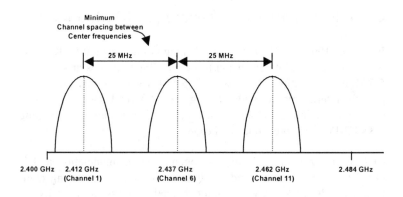

Figure 7-4 — Minimum Channel Spacing for IEEE 802.11 High Rate Networks

IEEE 802.11 DSSS High Rate Modulation and Data Rates

There are four modulation formats and data rates defined in IEEE 802.11b. The data rates include the basic rate, the extended rate, and enhanced rate. The basic rate is defined, as 1 Mbps modulated with DBPSK, and the extended rate is 2 Mbps DQPSK modulated. The 11-bit Barker word is used as the spreading format for the basic and extended rate as described for the DSSS PHY in Chapter 6. The enhanced rate is defined to operate at 5.5 Mbps and 11 Mbps using CCK modulation and packet binary convolutional coding (PBCC). PBCC is an option in the standard for those networks requiring enhanced performance. Frequency agility is another option defined in IEEE 802.11b. As with the 1 and 2 Mbps DSSS PHY, this option enables existing IEEE 802.11 FHSS 1 Mbps networks to be interoperable with 11 Mbps CCK high rate networks. The PBCC and frequency agility option are described later in the section.

Complementary Code Keying (CCK) Modulation

In July of 1998, the IEEE 802.11 Working Group adopted CCK as the basis for the high rate extension to deliver PSDU frames at speeds of 5.5 Mbp and 11 Mbps. CCK was adopted because it easily provides a path for interoperability with existing IEEE 802.11 1 and 2 Mbps systems by maintaining the same bandwidth and incorporating the existing DSSS PHY PLCP preamble and header.

CCK is a variation on M-ary orthogonal keying modulation and is based on an in-phase (I) and quadrature (Q) architecture using complex symbols. CCK allows for multichannel operation in the 2.4 GHz band by using the existing 1 and 2 Mbps DSSS channelization scheme. CCK uses 8 complex chips in each spreading code word. Each chip can assume one of four phases (QPSK). CCK uses 64 base spreading code words out of a possible set of 65536 (i.e., $65536-4^3$). Base spreading codes were chosen with good autocorrelation and cross-correlation properties. The CCK modulator chooses one of M unique for transmission of the scrambled PSDU. CCK uses one vector from a set of 64 complex quadrature phase shift keying (QPSK) vectors for the symbol and thereby modulates 6 bits (one of 64) on each spreading code symbol, as shown in Figure 7-5. Each spreading code is 8 complex chips in length. CCK uses a complex set of Walsh/Hadamard functions know as complementary codes. Refer to IEEE 802.11b for the equation used to derive the set of code words. There are four phase terms in the CCK equation. One of the terms modulates all of the chips, and this is used for the QPSK rotation of entire code vector. The others modulate every odd chip, every odd pair of chips and every odd quad of chips. To minimize DC offsets, the 4th and 7th terms in the equation are rotated by 180 degrees with a cover sequence. As with the IEEE 802.11 DSSS PHY, the phase rotation for CCK is counterclockwise. To insure that the modulation has the same bandwidth as the legacy IEEE 802.11 DSSS PHY, the chipping rate is kept at 11 Mbps while the symbol rate is increased to 1.375 Mbps. The spreading rate remains constant and only the data rate changes, and the CCK spectrum is the same as the legacy IEEE 802.11 waveform.

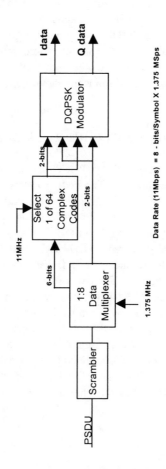

Figure 7-5—Generation of CCK Modulation

For 5.5 Mbps transmission, the scrambled binary bits of the PSDU are grouped into 4-bit nibbles, where two of the bits select the spreading function while the remaining two bits QPSK modulate the symbol, as illustrated in Figure 7-6. The spreading sequence then DQPSK modulates the carrier by driving the I and Q modulators. For 11 Mbps operation, the incoming scrambled PSDU binary bits are grouped into 2 and 6 bits. The 6 bits are used to select (one of 64) complex vectors of 8 chips in length for the symbol and the other 2 bits DQPSK modulate the entire symbol. The transmit waveform is the same, and the chipping rate is maintained at 11 Mbps.

DSSS Packet Binary Convolutional Coding

Packet binary convolutional coding (PBCC) is an optional coding scheme defined in IEEE 802.11b. The coding option uses a 64-state binary convolutional code (BCC), rate $R = 1/2$ code, and a cover sequence. The PBCC modulator is illustrated in Figure 7-7. The HR/DSSS PMD uses PBCC to transmit the PPDU. To ensure that the PPDU frame is properly decoded at the receiver, the BCC encoder's memory is cleared at the beginning and at the end of a frame. A cover sequence is used to map the QPSK symbols. The cover sequence is initialized with a 16-bit pattern (0011001110001011) to produce a 256-bit cover sequence, which selects the QPSK symbols. Binary phase shift keying (BPSK) is used for 5.5 Mbps, and QPSK for 11 Mbps. For QPSK each pair of output bits from the BCC is used to generate one symbol, conversely each pair of bits for BPSK produce two symbols. The result is one bit per symbol for QPSK and 1/2 bit for BPSK. Refer to IEEE 802.11b for the equation used for the cover sequence generator.

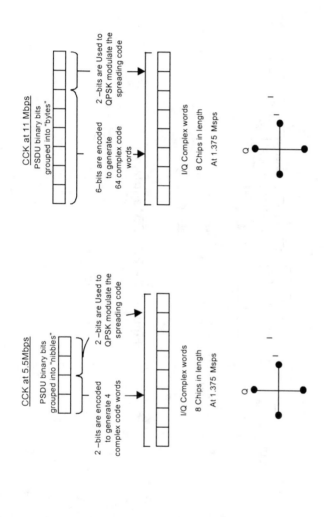

Figure 7-6 — The PSDU bit assignments and for CCK at 5.5 Mbps and 11 Mbps

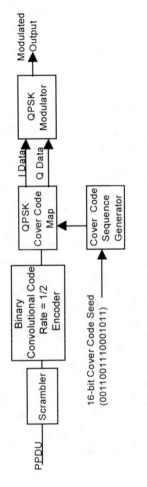

Figure 7-7 — PBCC Modulator

Frequency Hopped Spread Spectrum (FHSS) Interoperability

A channel agility option is defined in IEEE 802.11b which allows IEEE 802.11 FHSS 1 and 2 Mbps networks to interoperate with HR/DSSS 11 Mbps WLANs. Both nonoverlapping and overlapping high rate channels are supported. The nonoverlapping allows WLAN systems to operate simultaneously in the same area without interfering with each other. In North America channels 1, 6, and 11 are specified for nonoverlapping networks, and in Europe (excluding France and Spain) channels 1, 7, and 13 are specified. Two sets of hopping sequences are defined for worldwide operation. For more details on the hop patterns, refer to IEEE 802.11b.

Chapter 8
System Design Considerations for IEEE 802.11 WLANs

The IEEE 802.11 WLAN standard provides a number of physical layer options in terms of data rates, modulation types, and spreading spectrum techniques. Selecting the right physical layer and MAC technologies for your application requires careful planning and detailed systems analysis for developing the optimal WLAN implementation. It is impossible to include every possible system consideration in this handbook. However, we have focused on a few key issues we believe are important for consideration when implementing a compliant IEEE 802.11 interoperable WLAN system. The issues covered in this chapter are some of which the IEEE 802.11 Working Group focused on during the development of the standard.

The Medium

The difference between "wired" and RF WLANs is the radio communications link. While the radio communications link provides the freedom to move without constraints of wires, the wired media has the luxury of a controlled propagation media. Wireless RF medias are very difficult to control because the dynamics of the propagated signals over the media are constantly changing. This is the case for IEEE 802.11 WLANs because the 2.4 GHz bands are shared with unlicensed users. Radio system designers need to have a thorough understanding of the RF medium to properly design 2.4 GHz and 5 GHz IEEE 802.11 WLAN systems, especially for networks operating at data rates greater than 2 Mbps. The RF communication media for Home, Enterprise, and Manufacturing environments are very different and no two environments are the same. Multipath and Path loss are issues to consider when designing an IEEE 802.11 WLAN system.

Multipath

Multipath is one of the performance concerns for indoor IEEE 802.11 WLAN systems. Multipath occurs when the direct path of the transmitted signal is combined with paths of the reflected signal paths, resulting in a corrupted signal at the receiver, as show in Figure 8-1. The delay of the reflected signals is measured in nanoseconds (nsec), and is commonly known as delay spread. Delay spread is the parameter used to signify multipath. The amount of delay spread varies for indoors home, office, and manufacturing environments, as shown in Table 8-1. Surfaces of furniture, elevator shafts, walls, factory machinery, and metal constructed buildings all contribute to the amount of delay spread in a given environment.

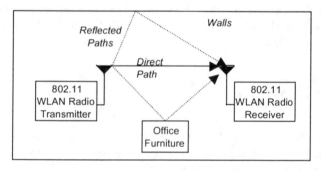

Figure 8-1 — How Multipath is Generated

The channel impulse response is a way to illustrate the amount of multipath dispersion. For example, the amount of delay spread in an office environment is approximately 100 nsec, as shown in Figure 8-2. Typically, energy reflected off the surface of walls causes the impulse response to have energy on the leading edge before the peak. The leading energy is called the precursor energy. The amount of precursor energy differs from one environment to the next. The processing required to correct the precursor energy is more complex than required for the trailing edge energy. The symbol period on the x-axis of the graph in Figure 8-2 is equal to the length of the 8 chip CCK code word. The 11 chip barker code is only 3 chips longer.

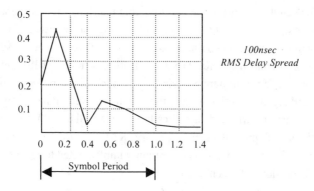

*100nsec
RMS Delay Spread*

Figure 8-2 — Impulse Channel Response Multipath (Delay Spread) for Office Environment

Table 8-1 — Typical Multipath Delay Spread for Indoor Environments

Environment	Delay Spread
Home	< 50 nsec
Office	~100 nsec
Manufacturing floor	200–300 nsec

RAKE processing and equalization are two methods used to process and resolve delay spread. A RAKE receiver is well-known architecture used to remove delay spreads on the order of 100 nsec. The RAKE is structured as a bank of correlators (fingers) with weighed delays and a combiner. Equalization is an alternative used to correct delay spreads greater than 100 nsec. Multipath causes the signals from the previous symbol to interfere with the signals of the next. This is known as intersymbol interference (ISI). As with ISI, interchip interference (ICI) results when the signals of the previous chip interfere with the signals of the next chip. ISI and ICI are issues for higher data rate systems because the symbol and chip periods are shorter. This is the case for IEEE 802.11a and IEEE 802.11b. Equalization corrects for ISI and ICI. An equalizer is a multitapped delay line, which takes the delayed and attenuated signal subtracted from the actual received signal. However, for environments where delay spreads are greater than 200 nsec, more complex signal processing is necessary. RAKE processing combined with ISI and ICI equalization is commonly implemented to resolve multipath dispersions of this magnitude.

Multipath Channel Model

In an environment where performance measurements of the same radio are used, in the same location, the results may not agree. This is due to the changing position of people in the room and slight changes in the environment, can produce significant changes in the signal power at the radio receiver. A consistent channel model is required to allow comparison of different WLAN systems and to provide consistent results. In doing so, the IEEE 802.11 Working Group adopted the following channel model as the baseline for predicting multipath for modulations used in IEEE 802.11a (5 GHz) and IEEE 802.11b (2.4 GHz). This model is ideal for software simulations predicting performance results of a given implementation. The channel impulse response illustrated in Figure 8-3 is composed of complex samples with random uniformly distributed phase and Rayleigh distributed magnitude with average power decaying exponentially.

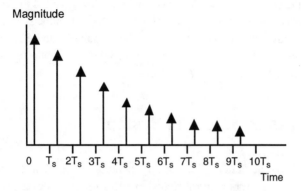

Figure 8-3 — Channel Impulse Response for IEEE 802.11a and IEEE 802.11b

The mathematical model for the channel is as follows

$$h_k = N\left(0, \frac{1}{2}\sigma_k^2\right) + jN\left(0, \frac{1}{2}\sigma_k^2\right)$$

$$\sigma_k^2 = \sigma_0^2 e^{-kT_s/T_{RMS}}$$

$$\sigma_0^2 = 1 - e^{-T_s/T_{RMS}}$$

Where $N\left(0, \frac{1}{2}\sigma_k^2\right)$ is a zero mean Gaussian random variable with variance $\frac{1}{2}\sigma_k^2$ produced by generating an N(0, 1) and multiplying it by $\sigma_k/\sqrt{2}$), and $\sigma_0^2 = 1 - e^{-T_s/T_{RMS}}$ is chosen so that the condition $\sigma_k^2 = 1$ is satisfied to ensure same average received power.

Let T_s be the sampling period and T_{RMS} be the delay spread of the channel. The performance assessment shall be no longer than the smaller of 1/(signal bandwidth) or $T_{RMS}/2$. The number of samples to be taken in the impulse response should ensure sufficient decay of the impulse response tail, e.g. $k_{max} = 10 \times T_{RMS}/T_s$.

Path Loss in a WLAN System

Another key consideration is the issue of operating range relative to path loss. This plays an important role in determining the size of overlapping WLAN cells and distribution of APs. Path loss calculations are equally important for determining the radio's receiver sensitivity and transmitting power level and signal to noise ratio (SNR) requirements. As radios transmit signals to other receivers in a given area, the signal attenuates as a square of the distance (D). The distance is the radius of a WLAN cell, as shown in Figure 8-4. The wavelength (lambda) is the ratio between the speed of light and the signal frequency. As the receiver moves away from the transmitter, the receiver's signal power decays until it reaches the receiver's noise floor, at which time the bit error rate becomes unacceptable. For indoor applications beyond 20 feet, propagation losses increase at about 30 dB per 100 feet. This occurs because of a combination of attenuation by walls, ceilings, and furniture. Each wall constructed with sheet rock and wood typically attenuates the signal by 6 dB and walls constructed with cement block walls attenuate the signal by 4 dB. However, additional losses may occur depending on the fading characteristics of the operating environment, which we describe in the next section. The same path loss principles apply for all frequency bands. However, as the operating frequency increases from 2.4 GHz to 5 GHz, for example, an additional path loss of 5–10 dB occurs. This results in a smaller cell radius and may require additional overlapping cells and APs to guarantee the same area as a system operating at 2.4 GHz.

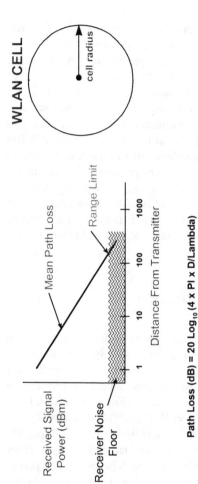

Path Loss (dB) = $20 \log_{10} (4 \times PI \times D/\text{Lambda})$

Where:

r = D is the radius of the WLAN cell

Lambda = c/f

where : c = speed of light ($3 \times 10^8 \text{ms}^{-1}$)

f = signal frequency in Hz

Figure 8-4 — Free Space Path Loss Model

Multipath Fading

Another key consideration is the path loss due to multipath fading. Multipath fading occurs when the reflected signal paths refract off people, furniture, windows, and walls, and scatter the transmitted signal. For example, moving the receiver from the transmitter a small distance even only a few inches, can produce an additional loss of signal power on the order of 20 dB or more. Multipath fading is viewed as two separate factors and described as probability distribution functions. The first factor is a characteristic known as log normal fading. These are coefficient products which result as the signal reflects off surfaces and propagates to the receiver. As the signal coefficients product propagate to the receiver, they are summed together with the direct path where they cancel each other, causing significant attention of the transmitted signal. This is the second factor, known as Rayleigh fading. As previously, mentioned RAKE architectures and equalization are techniques used to correct for these effects.

Es/No vs BER Performance

System performance tradeoffs are often made in the decision process when selecting a modulation type and data rate. System tradeoffs in terms of receiver sensitivity, range, and transmit power become very important for developing low cost implementations, especially for higher rate 2.4 GHz IEEE 802.11b systems. Figure 8-5 illustrates a comparison of the theoretical Es/No vs BER curves for uncoded QPSK, PBCC 5.5–11 Mbps, CCK 5.5–11 Mbps, and Barker 1 and 2 Mbps. The theoretical curves include additive white gaussian (AWG) noise in the channel. These curves are provided as a guide to assess the performance for a complete system implementing CCK and PBCC. However to get better understanding of the overall systems performance, other factors such as multipath, signal fading, carrier phase noise, noise figure, and other implementation losses should be considered in the link budget as part of the systems analysis.

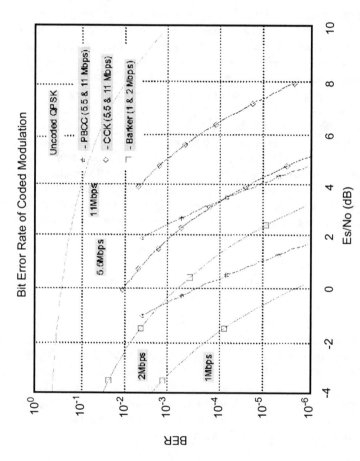

Figure 8-5 — Theoretical Eb/No vs BER with AGW for 2.4 GHz IEEE 802.11b

Data Rate vs Aggregate Throughput

The IEEE 802.11 standard defines data rate in terms of symbol rate, or available bit rate. The PPDU data is modulated and transmitted over the RF or IR medium at this rate. This rate is often confused with the aggregate data throughput. The aggregate data rate, takes into account the overhead associated with protocol frame structure, collisions, and implementation processing delays associated with frames processed by mobile stations and APs. Simulations may be run in software to estimate the aggregate throughput of the protocol and benchmarked against compliant IEEE 802.11 WLAN systems. However, calculating the aggregate throughput can be complex because there are a number of detailed variables to consider. The protocol overhead includes parameters such as RTS, CTS, ACK frames, (SIF, DIFs, PIFs) interframe space timing, beacon periods and random back-off periods, estimated collisions, PPDU frame size, and RF propagation delays. A good rule of thumb for estimating the average aggregate throughput of an IEEE 802.11 wireless network is 75% of the data rate for DCF operation, and 85% of the data rate for PCF.

WLAN Installation and Site Survey

Many installations begin with a site survey. A site survey serves a number of purposes. First, the survey is used to determine the maximum operating range between an AP (fixed location) and mobile stations for a specified transmit RF power level. Second, the survey helps identify holes of coverage due to multipath, interference sources, and neighboring existing WLAN installations. Lastly, it is used in cell planning of overlapping BSAs and for layout of APs giving them hardwired access to existing wired Ethernet LAN infrastructures.

Today, many equipment manufactures have tests built in to their products to conduct such surveys. PC laptops with IEEE 802.11 WLAN adaptor cards, with embedded software tools, are commonly used. In some cases, a spectrum analyzer with special directional antennas is used to measure path loss through walls and other obstructions and to pinpoint and identify interference sources. Some of the tests include BER and PER, and link quality measurements as a function of range. Typically, the tests are recorded using a pair of WLAN adaptors; one is set up in a fixed location and the other as a mobile station. Every environment is different and the number of APs required for a given installation depends upon the number of holes in the coverage area due to multipath, and signal attenuation through walls, ceilings, and floors. However, on average, for indoor operation, the maximum operating distance between a mobile station and an AP operating in the 2.4 GHz frequency, transmitting at an RF transmit power of +20 dBm (100 mW) at data rates of 1 and 2 Mbps, yields approximately 400 feet and 100 feet at 11 Mbps.

Interference in the 2.4 GHz Frequency Band

The microwave oven used in household and commercial kitchens is the main interference source in the 2.4 GHz unlicensed frequency band. The magnetron tubes used in the microwave ovens radiate a continuous-wave-like (CW-like) interference that sweeps over tens of megahertz (MHz) of the 2.4–2.483 GHz band during the positive half cycle of ac line voltage. The microwave oven's EIRP has a maximum ranging between 16 and 33 dBm. The power cycle frequency is 50 Hz 20 msec or 60 Hz 16 msec depending upon the geographical location. In North America, the ac line frequency is 60 Hz and the microwave oven's magnetron pulses on for 8 msec and off for 8 msec. The maximum packet length defined in the IEEE 802.11 protocol was designed to operate between the 8 msec pulses of the microwave energy.

Other sources of interference include neighboring in-band radios. Two types of interference are considered here. First is cochannel interference, which is induced from radios from adjacent cells that are on the same channel frequency. Proper cell planning of the channel frequency and hopping patterns and careful layout of the APs can minimize this interference. The second type of interference is from other systems such as neighboring DSSS and FHSS WLAN networks. Built into the standard are three mechanisms used to help minimize the amount of interference. The first is the clear channel assessment, where the MAC layer protocol provides a method of collision avoidance. The second is processing gain, which provides some protection from FHSS radios, whose spectrum appears as narrowband interferers. The third are the hop patterns; there is sufficient frequency spacing between pseudorandom hops to minimize the interference due to neighboring DSSS channels. To some degree, legacy 2.4 GHz IEEE 802.11-compliant FHSS and DSSS systems and IEEE 802.11b high-rate WLAN systems do coexist. However, careful cell planning will help minimize the amount of interference a system will experience especially at the outer fringe of the cell.

Antenna Diversity

Historically antenna diversity has been an effective low-cost alternative solution used to combat and mitigate the effects of multipath and delay spread in WLAN radio receivers. It is relatively easy to implement in the mobile stations and APs and does not require the signal processing hardware used in other diversity techniques. The object behind antenna diversity is to space the antennas apart from each other to minimize the effects of the uncorrelated multipath at the receiver. Spacing the antennas far apart allows the receiver to pick and demodulate the larger signal of the two signals. For 2.4 GHz IEEE 802.11 implementations, the bit length of the preamble sync fields was selected based on these criteria. The antennas are typically spaced anywhere from 0.25l to several lambdas (wavelengths) apart. The amount of separation depends upon the amount of delay-spread tolerance required for the system to operate in a given operating environment. Adding antenna diversity will improve the packet error rate (PER) performance of a wireless link by 2 to 1, as well as improve the availability of the link. There are a number of 2.4 GHz antennas on the market today with different configurations. Patch antennas are commonly used at the mobile client PCMCIA implements, because of cost and size constraints. On the other hand, omni-directional antennas are used at the AP because they provide the optimal antenna coverage. Although antenna diversity is an option in the standard, as a minimum, antenna diversity should always be consider at the AP, as shown in Figure 8-6. This form of diversity will minimize the risk of packet loss due to multipath and interference, and ensure optimal throughput performance in a system.

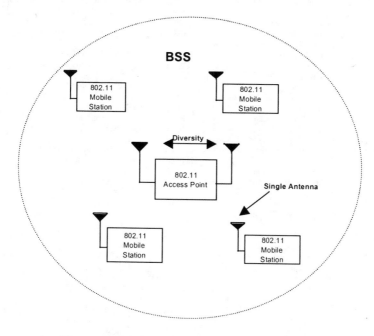

**Figure 8-6 — Antenna Diversity at the AP
as a Minimum**

Acronyms and Abbreviations

ACK	acknowledgment frame	ISI	intersymbol interference
AGC	automatic gain control	ISM	industrial, scientific, and medical
AID	association identifier	LBT	"listen before talk"
AP	access point	LLC	logical link control
ATIM	announcement traffic indication message	MAC	medium access control
		MIB	management information base
BCC	binary convolutional code	MKK	Ministery of Telecommunications
BPSK	binary phase shift keying	MMACS	Multimedia Mobile Access Communication System
BSS	basic service set		
BSSID	basic service set identifier	MPDU	MAC protocol data unit
CDMA	code division multiple access	MSDU	MAC service data unit
CF-End	contention-free end	NAV	network allocation vector
CFP	contention-free period	NIC	network interface card
CF-Poll	contention-free poll	OFDM	orthogonal frequency domain multiplexing
CSMA/CA	carrier sense multiple access with collision avoidance		
		OFDM PHY	OFDM physical layer
CTS	clear to send	PBCC	packet binary convolutional coding
DA	destination address		
dB	decibels	PC	point coordinator
DBPSK	differential binary phase shift keying	PCF	point coordination function
		PHY	physical, physical layer
DCF	distributed coordination function	PIFS	priority interframe space
DIFS	distributed interframe space	PLCP	physical layer convergence procedure
DPSK	differential phase shift keying		
DQPSK	differential quadrature phase shift keying	PMD	physical medium dependent
		PPDU	PLCP protocol data unit
DS	distribution system	PPM	pulse position modulation
DSSS	direct sequence spread spectrum	PSDU	PLCP service data unit
EIFS	extended interframe space	PSF	PLCP signaling field
ESS	extended service set	PS-Poll	power save poll
ETSI	European Telecommunications Standards Institute	QAM	Quadrature Amplitude Modulation
		QPSK	quadrature phase shift keying
FCC	Federal Communications Commission	RA	receiver address
		RF	radio frequency
FCS	frame check sequence	RFID	radio frequency ID
FFT	fast fourier transform	RSADSI	RSA Data Security, Inc.
FHSS	frequency hopping spread spectrum	RTS	request to send
		SA	source address
GFSK	Gaussian frequency shift key	SFD	start of frame delimiter
GPS	global positioning system	SIFS	short interframe space
HR/DSSS	high rate direct sequence spread spectrum	SNR	signal to noise ratio
		SSID	service set identity
I/Q	interphase/quadrature	STA	station
IAPP	inter-access point protocol	TA	transmitter address
IBSS	independent basic service set	TBTT	target beacon transmission time
ICI	interchip interference	TIM	traffic indication map
ICV	integrity check value	TSF	timer synchronization factor
IEEE	Institute of Electrical and Electronics Engineers	TU	time units
		WLAN	wireless LAN
IR	infrared		